Foreword

The title of this collection of songs speaks for itself. The songs have been selected on the basis of their popular appeal with pickin' and singin' groups and individuals. In order to provide as many songs as possible within the limitations of a book of this size the pages have not been burdened with "how to play the guitar" instructions, anecdotes or background notes of more or less questionable reliability on folk-song research, or lessons in history.

Realizing it is impossible to please everyone all of the time, a careful attempt has been made to please anyone most of the time. You will find a balance between old favorites, new favorites, and fresh songs and a wide variety of kinds of songs to fit many different moods, tastes, and occasions. We have omitted the clichés which riddle the pages of community song books, and avoided difficult-to-sing, esoteric songs which appeal primarily to folk-song collectors, or songs which might be included because of their historical significance.

Since many people use a song book only for the "extra verses" we have made no attempt to cut down on them, and have, in fact, included many extra verses not usually found in print which add new dimensions to old favorites. See, for example, *Paper of Pins*, *Billy Boy*, and *I've Been Workin' on the Railroad*. Guitar chords are indicated for all of the songs so they may be accompanied by guitar, ukelele, autoharp, and other chording instruments as well as by piano and organ by those who play by a chord system.

The songs have been arranged in what might be called a psychological order. It has been assumed that you will prefer to browse through the book until you find a song that strikes your fancy, but that when you find it you may wish to have a similar song nearby. We have not created artificial divisions and categories, however, on the grounds that one person's new favorite is another person's old favorite and not even a favorite of someone else; a song with a sea theme is not necessarily a sea song, and so on. For the guidance of those who prefer an ordered presentation the following breakdown is suggested:

The book begins with folk songs and ballads (we won't take up space to argue the definition), many of which are new favorites to those who have lately discovered the folk song during its recent revival. Many of them, of course, are old favorites for afficionados of long standing. Although many American songs come from British Isles folk-song tradition there are some that have more strictly maintained their original identity. These begin with *Gently, Johnny, My Jingalo* and continue through *Cockles and Mussels*. Songs that might be closely associated with the drinking crowd start with *The Cat and the Mouse*. *Worried Man Blues* heads up a set of songs with a blues flavor. The college campus has developed a folk-song tradition of its own and many of these songs have been included, beginning with *The Poor and the Rich*. The campus songs include a few sick songs such as *Away With Rum* and others. *John Jacob Jingleheimer Schmidt* is followed by other repetitive songs and those memory-stretching cumulative songs for the more versatile singers, including the old masters, *Green Grow the Rushes* and *The Twelve Days of Christmas*. Sea songs and songs about the sea for landlubbers begin with *Goodbye, My Lover, Goodbye*. *Bury Me Not on the Lone Prairie* introduces some favorite cowboy and western songs. The last group contains gospel and spiritual favorites.

Remember our warning that these are artificial categories and don't be surprised if you find a song in any group that could be just as properly or improperly included in some other group.

So much for writin'. The rest of this book is devoted to pickin' and singin'.

Songs for
Pickin' and Singin'

An Original Gold Medal Collection

Edited by

James F. Leisy

GOLD MEDAL BOOKS

FAWCETT PUBLICATIONS, INC., GREENWICH, CONN.
MEMBER OF AMERICAN BOOK PUBLISHERS COUNCIL, INC.

Contents

Listed alphabetically under each heading

FOLK SONGS AND BALLADS

FROM THE BRITISH ISLES

FOR THE DRINKING CROWD

SEA SONGS

COWBOY AND WESTERN

GOSPEL AND SPIRITUAL

Sinner Man

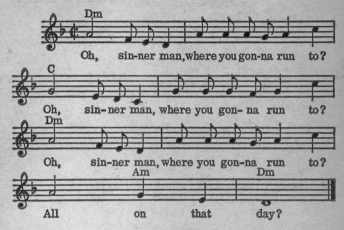

Oh, sin-ner man, where you gon-na run to?

Oh, sin-ner man, where you gon-na run to?

Oh, sin-ner man, where you gon-na run to?

All on that day?

2. Run to the rock, the rock was a-melting, (3 times)
All on that day.

3. Run to the sea, the sea was a-boiling, (3 times)
All on that day.

4. Run to the moon, the moon was a-bleeding, (3 times)
All on that day.

5. Run to the Lord, "Lord, won't you hide me?" (3 times)
All on that day.

6. Run to the Devil, Devil was a-waiting. (3 times)
All on that day.

7. Oh, sinner man, you oughta been a-praying, (3 times)
All on that day.

Darlin' Corey

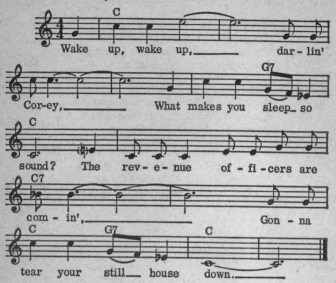

Wake up, wake up,_____ dar-lin' Cor-ey,_____ What makes you sleep so sound? The rev-e-nue of-fi-cers are com-in',_____ Gon-na tear your still__ house down._____

2. Go 'way, go 'way, darlin' Corey,
   Quit hangin' 'round my bed.
   Pretty women run me distracted,
   Corn likker's killin' me dead.

3. The first time I saw darlin' Corey,
   She was standin' in the door;
   Her shoes and stockin's in her hands,
   And her feet all over the floor.

4. The next time I saw darlin' Corey,
   She was standin' by the banks of the sea;
   She had a pistol strapped around her body,
   And a banjo on her knee.

5. The last time I saw darlin' Corey,
   She had a wine glass in her hand.
   She was drinkin' that sweet pizen likker,
   With a low-down gamblin' man.

6. Dig a hole, dig a hole in the meadow,
   Dig a hole in the cold, cold ground,
   Go and dig me a hole in the meadow
   Just to lay darlin' Corey down.

7. Don't you hear them bluebirds a-singin'?
   Don't you hear that mournful sound?
   They're preachin' Corey's funeral
   In the lonesome graveyard ground.

Deep Blue Sea

Deep blue sea, ba-by, deep blue sea, Deep blue sea, ba-by, deep blue sea, Deep blue sea, ba-by, deep blue sea, It was Wil-lie what got drown-ded in the deep blue sea.

2. Lower him down with a golden chain. (3 times)
   It was Willie what got drownded in the
   deep blue sea.

3. Dig his grave with a silver spade. (3 times)
   It was Willie what got drownded in the
   deep blue sea.

4. Wrap him up in a silken shroud. (3 times)
   It was Willie what got drownded in the
   deep blue sea.

5. Golden sun bring him back to me. (3 times)
   It was Willie what got drownded in the
   deep blue sea.

Fond Affection

Once you loved with fond af -
fect - ion, Once your thoughts were all of
me. Now you've gone to seek a -
noth-er, And you care no more for me.

2. You gave back your ring and letters,
   And the picture I loved so well,
   Now each time, we meet as strangers,
   But I still can't say farewell.

3. Once you loved with fond affection,
   Once your thoughts were all of me,
   Now you've gone to seek another,
   And you care no more for me.

Hush, Little Baby

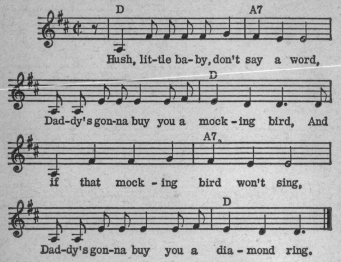

Hush, lit-tle ba-by, don't say a word,

Dad-dy's gon-na buy you a mock-ing bird, And

if that mock-ing bird won't sing,

Dad-dy's gon-na buy you a dia-mond ring.

2. And if that diamond ring turns brass,
Daddy's gonna buy you a looking glass,
And if that looking glass gets broke,
Daddy's gonna buy you a billy goat.

3. And if that billy goat won't pull,
Daddy's gonna buy you a cart and bull,
And if that cart and bull turn over,
Daddy's gonna buy you a dog named Rover.

4. And if that dog named Rover won't bark,
Daddy's gonna buy you a horse and cart,
And if that horse and cart fall down,
You'll still be the sweetest little baby in town.

Bury Me Beneath the Willow

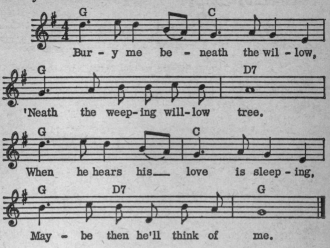

Bur - y me be - neath the wil - low,

'Neath the weep-ing will-low tree.

When he hears his___ love is sleep - ing,

May - be then he'll think of me.

2. My heart is sad and I am lonely,
Thinking of the one I love.
Will I see him never, never,
Till we meet in Heaven above. (Chorus)

3. He told me that he dearly loved me,
How could I believe him untrue.
Then one day some neighbors told me,
He has proven untrue to you. (Chorus)

4. Tomorrow was to be our wedding.
I pray: Oh, Lord, where can he be?
He's gone, he's gone to love another.
He no longer cares for me. (Chorus)

The House of the Rising Sun

There is a house in New Orleans They call the Rising Sun. It's been the ru-in of man-y a poor girl, And I, oh Lord, was one.

2. If I had a-listened to what mama said,
   I'd be at home today.
   But I was young and foolish, poor girl,
   I let a gambler lead me astray.

3. My mother, she's a tailor,
   She sews those new blue jeans.
   My sweetheart is a drunkard, Lord,
   He drinks down in New Orleans.

4. Go tell my baby sister:
   "Don't do what your sister done,
   Stay away from that house in New Orleans,
   They call the Rising Sun."

5. With one foot on the platform,
   And the other one on the train.
   I'm goin' back to New Orleans
   To wear the ball and chain.

6. I'm goin' back to New Orleans,
   My race is almost run.
   I'm goin' back to spend my life
   Beneath that risin' sun.

Let Her Go

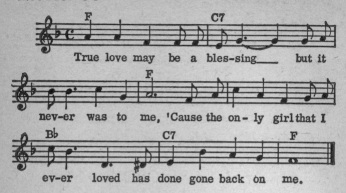

True love may be a bles-sing___ but it
nev-er was to me, 'Cause the on- ly girl that I
ev-er loved has done gone back on me.

2. Let her go, let her go, God Bless her,
Wherever she may be,
She can look this wide world over,
But she'll never find a man like me.

3. There may be a change in the weather,
There may be a change in the sea,
But the only change my true love has
Is the change she took from me.

4. So, here's to a good glass of whiskey;
Here's to a good glass of beer;
They're not half as sweet as a maiden's kiss,
But a damn sight more sincere.

Delia's Gone

Ton-y shot his Del-ia, 'Twas on a Christ-mas night; First thing she did was hang her head and die.

Chorus
Del-ia's gone, one more round, Del-ia's gone, one more round, Del-ia's round.

2. Delia, Delia,
   Where you been so long?
   Everybody's talkin' about
   Poor Delia's dead and gone. (Chorus)

3. Sent for the doctor.
   Doctor came too late.
   Sent for the minister
   To lay out Delia straight. (Chorus)

Words and music by Blind Blake (Blake Alphonso Higgs)
Copyright 1954 by Hollis Music, Inc., New York, N. Y.
USED BY PERMISSION

Bay of Mexico

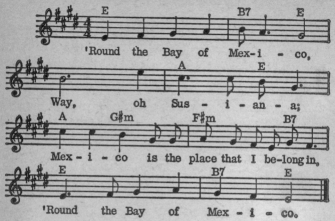

'Round the Bay of Mex-i-co,

Way, oh Sus-i-an-a;

Mex-i-co is the place that I be-long in,

'Round the Bay of Mex-i-co.

2. When I was a young man in my prime,
   Way, oh Susianna;
   I'd court those Nassau gals two at a time
   'Round the Bay of Mexico. (Chorus)

3. Nassau girls they love me so,
   Way, oh Susianna;
   'Cause I don't say everything that I know
   'Round the Bay of Mexico.

4. Nassau gals don't use no combs,
   Way, oh Susianna;
   They comb their hair with whipper snapper bones
   'Round the Bay of Mexico.

5. Nassau boys don't use no sleds,
   Way, oh Susianna;
   They slide down the hills on whipper snapper heads,
   'Round the Bay of Mexico.

6. Goodbye girls of Nassau town,
   Way, oh Susianna;
   I'm bound away for the fishing ground
   'Round the Bay of Mexico.

New lyric by Paul Campbell; new music by Tom Geraci
Copyright 1953 by Folkways Music Publishers, Inc., New York, N. Y.
USED BY PERMISSION

Michael, Row the Boat Ashore

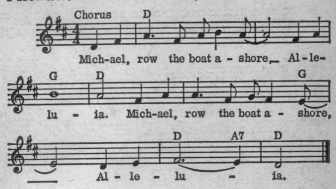

2. Michael's boat's a music boat, Alleluia,
   Michael's boat's a music boat, Alleluia. (Chorus)

3. Sister, help to trim the sail, Alleluia,
   Sister, help to trim the sail, Alleluia. (Chorus)

4. Jordan's River is deep and wide, Alleluia,
   Jordan's River is deep and wide, Alleluia. (Chorus)

5. Jordan's River is chilly and cold, Alleluia,
   Jordan's River is chilly and cold, Alleluia. (Chorus)

Puttin' on the Style©

Two wheels 'round a cor - ner,

Driv-ing like he's mad, Young man in an

aut - o, He bor - rowed from his

dad, He honks his horn so loud - ly To

see his girl friend smile, But she knows he's

on - ly Put-ting on the style.

Chorus

Put-ting on the ag - o - ny,

Put-ting on the style. That's what ev-'ry-

bo - dy's Do-ing all the while. And

22

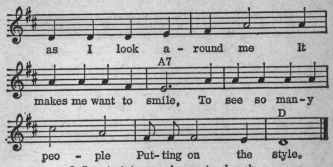

as I look a - round me It
makes me want to smile, To see so man-y
A7
peo - ple Put- ting on the style.
D

2. Sweet sixteen and goes to church
   Just to see the boys;
   See her laugh and giggle
   At every little noise.
   She turns her head a little
   And stands that way awhile,
   But everybody knows she's only
   Putting on the style. (Chorus)

3. Young man home from college
   Makes a big display
   With a giant jawbreaker
   That he can hardly say;
   It can't be found in Webster
   And won't be for awhile,
   But everybody knows he's only
   Putting on the style. (Chorus)

New words and new music arr. by Norman Cazden
Additional lyrics by Frank Lynn
Copyright 1957 by Melody Trails, Inc., New York, N. Y.
USED BY PERMISSION

The Titanic

Oh they built the ship Ti - tan - ic to
sail the o - cean blue. And they
thought they had a ship that the sea would not leak thro'. But the
Lord's al - might - y hand knew this
ship would nev - er stand. It was
sad when that great ship went down.

Chorus
Oh, it was sad, Lord, sad; Oh, it was
sad, Lord, sad; It was sad when that great ship went
down, to the bot-tom of the.. Hus-bands and wives, lit-tle
chil - dren lost their lives, It was
sad when that great ship went down.

Oh, they sailed from England, and were almost to the shore,
When the rich refused to associate with the pore,
So they put them down below, where they were the first to go.
It was sad when that great ship went down. (Chorus)

The boat was full of sin, and the sides about to burst,
When the captain shouted: "Women and children first!"
Oh, the captain tried to wire, but the lines were all afire.
It was sad when that great ship went down.

When they swung the lifeboats out on the deep and raging sea,
And the band struck up with "Nearer My God to Thee,"
Little children wept and cried, and the waves swept o'er the side.
It was sad when that great ship went down.

The Wabash Cannonball

From the great At - lan - tic O - cean, To the wide Pa - cif - ic shore, From the queen of flow-ing moun - tains To the south - land by the shore, She's might - y tall and hand-some And quite well known by all, She's the com - bi - na - tion of The Wa - bash Can - non - ball.

2. Listen to the jingle,
The rumble and the roar
As she glides along the woodland,
Through the hills and by the shore,
Hear the mighty rush of the engine,
Hear that lonesome hobo squall,
You're traveling through the jungles on
The Wabash Cannonball.

3. She come down from Birmingham
   One cold December day,
   As she rolled into the station,
   You could hear the people say,
   There's a girl from Birmingham,
   She's long and she is tall,
   She come down from Birmingham on
   The Wabash Cannonball.

4. Here's to Daddy Claxon,
   May his name forever stand,
   And always be remembered in
   The courts of Alabam,
   His earthly race is over
   And the curtains round him fall,
   We'll carry him home to victory on
   The Wabash Cannonball.

I'm Going Down the Road Feeling Bad

2. I'm goin' where the climate suits my clothes,
   I'm goin' where the climate suits my clothes,
   I'm goin' where the climate suits my clothes, Lord, Lord,
   And I ain't gonna be treated this a-way.

3. I'm a-lookin' for a job with honest pay,
   I'm a-lookin' for a job with honest pay,
   I'm a-lookin' for a job with honest pay, Lord, Lord,
   And I ain't gonna be treated this a-way.

4. These two dollar shoes hurt my feet,
   These two dollar shoes hurt my feet,
   These two dollar shoes hurt my feet, Lord, Lord,
   And I ain't gonna be treated this a-way.

5. But ten dollar shoes fit 'em neat,
   But ten dollar shoes fit 'em neat,
   But ten dollar shoes fit 'em neat, Lord, Lord,
   And I ain't gonna be treated this a-way.

6. I'm down in the jailhouse on my knees,
   I'm down in the jailhouse on my knees,
   I'm down in the jailhouse on my knees, Lord, Lord,
   And I ain't gonna be treated this a-way.

7. I'm leaving if I never come back,
   I'm leaving if I never come back,
   I'm leaving if I never come back, Lord, Lord,
   And I ain't gonna be treated this a-way.

8. I'm goin' down the road feelin' bad,
   I'm goin' down the road feelin' bad,
   I'm goin' down the road feelin' bad, Lord, Lord,
   And I ain't gonna be treated this a-way.

Acres of Clams

2. For one who got rich by mining
   I saw there were hundreds grew poor;
   I made up my mind to try farming,
   The only pursuit that is sure.

3. The only pursuit that is sure,
   The only pursuit that is sure,
   I made up my mind to try farming,
   The only pursuit that is sure.

4. I rolled up my grub in my blanket,
   I left all my tools on the ground,
   I started one morning to shank it
   For the country they call Puget Sound.

5. No longer the slave of ambition,
   I laugh at the world and its shams,
   And think of my happy condition
   Surrounded by acres of clams.

6. Surrounded by acres of clams,
   Surrounded by acres of clams,
   And think of my happy condition
   Surrounded by acres of clams.

Cindy

You ought to see my Cin-dy, She lives_ way down south; She's so sweet the hon-ey bees Swarm a-round her mouth. Get a-long home, Cin-dy, Cin-dy, Get a-long home, Cin-dy, Cin-dy, Get a-long home, Cin-dy, Cin-dy, I'll mar-ry you some day.

2. The first I seen my Cindy
   She was standing in the door,
   Her shoes and stockings in her hand,
   Her feet all over the floor. (Chorus)

3. She took me to her parlor,
   She cooled me with her fan;
   She said I was the prettiest thing
   In the shape of mortal man. (Chorus)

4. She kissed me and she hugged me,
   She called me sugar plum;
   She throwed her arms around me,
   I thought my time had come. (Chorus)

5. Oh, Cindy is a pretty girl,
   Cindy is a peach.
   She threw her arms around my neck,
   And hung on like a leech. (Chorus)

6. And if I was a sugar tree
   Standing in the town,
   Every time my Cindy passed
   I'd shake some sugar down. (Chorus)

7. And if I had a thread and needle
   Fine as I could sew,
   I'd sew that gal to my coat tails
   And down the road I'd go. (Chorus)

8. I wish I was an apple
   A-hanging on a tree,
   Every time that Cindy passed,
   She'd take a bite of me. (Chorus)

All Night Long

All night long,_____ all night long,_____ all night long,_____ from mid-night on._____ Down in the sta-tion,_____ read-y to go;_____ If the train don't come,_____ some-thing's wrong on the road._____

2. If I live and don't get killed,
   I'll make my home in Louisville.

3. I'd rather be dead and in my grave,
   Than in this old town treated this way.

4. If anyone asks you who wrote this song,
   Tell 'em 'twas me (and I sing it) all night long.

Follow the Drinkin' Gourd©

Chorus

Fol - low___ the drink - in' gourd,___

Fol - low___ the drink.- in' gourd,___ For the

old man is a-wait-in' For to car-ry you to free-dom,

Fol - low the drink - in' gourd.

Verse

When the sun comes up and the first quail calls___

Fol-low the drink - in' gourd. The

old man is a-wait-in' For to car-ry you to free-dom,

Fol - low the drink - in' gourd.

The river bank'll make a mighty good road,
The dead trees will show you the way.
Left foot, peg foot, travelin' on,
Follow the drinkin' gourd.

The river ends between two hills,
Follow the drinkin' gourd.
There's another river on the other side,
Follow the drinkin' gourd.

Words and music by Paul Campbell
Copyright 1951 by Folkways Music Publishers, Inc., New York, N. Y.
USED BY PERMISSION

Stagolee

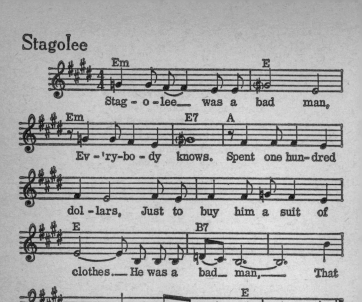

Stag - o - lee__ was a bad man, Ev - 'ry-bo - dy knows. Spent one hun- dred dol - lars, Just to buy him a suit of clothes.__ He was a bad__ man,____ That mean old Stag - o - lee.__

2. Stagolee shot Billy de Lyons
   What do you think about that,
   Shot him down in cold blood
   Because he stole his Stetson hat;
   He was a bad man
   That mead old Stagolee.

3. Billy de Lyons said, Stagolee
   Please don't take my life,
   I've got two little babes
   And a darling, loving wife;
   You are a bad man
   You mean old Stagolee.

4. What do I care about your wife
   Your two little darling babes,
   You done stole my Stetson hat
   I'm bound to take your life;
       He was a bad man
       That mean old Stagolee.

5. The judge said, Stagolee
   What you doing in here,
   You done shot Mr. Billy de Lyons
   You going to die in the electric chair;
       He was a bad man
       That mean old Stagolee.

6. Twelve o'clock they killed him
   Head reached up high,
   Last thing that poor boy said
   My six-shooter never lied.
       He was a bad man
       That mean old Stagolee.

The Willow Tree

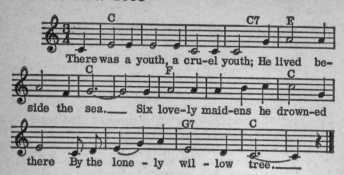

There was a youth, a cru-el youth; He lived be-side the sea.___ Six love-ly maid-ens he drown-ed there By the lone - ly wil - low tree.___

2. As he went out with Sally Brown,
   And they walked by the sea,
   An evil thought it came to him
   By that lonely willow tree.

3. "Now turn your back to the waterside,
   Your face to the willow tree;
   Six pretty maidens I've drowned them here,
   And you the seventh shall be.

4. "But first take off your golden gown,
   Take off your gown," said he;
   "For though I am going to murder you,
   I would not spoil your finery."

5. "Then turn around, you false young man,
   Then turn around, said she;
   "For it is not proper that such a youth
   A naked woman should see."

6. Then 'round he turned, that false young man,
   Around about turned he,
   And seizing him boldly in both her arms,
   She cast him into the sea.

7. "Lie there, lie there, you false young man,
   Lie there, lie there," said she;
   "For six pretty maidens you've drowned them here,
   Go, keep them company."

8. He sank beneath the icy waves,
   He sank down into the sea;
   No living thing wept a tear for him
   Save that lonely willow tree.

Banks of the Ohio

I asked my love to go with me, to take a walk a lit-tle way; And as we walked, and as we talked a-bout our gold-en wed-ding day

Chorus

2. Then only say that you'll be mine,
   In no other arms entwined.
   Down beside where the waters flow,
   On the banks of the Ohio.

3. I asked your mother for you, dear,
   And she said you were too young;
   Only say that you'll be mine--
   Happiness in my home you'll find.

4. I held a knife against her breast
   And gently in my arms she pressed,
   Crying: "Willie, oh Willie, don't murder me,
   For I'm unprepared for eternity.

5. I took her by her lily white hand,
   Led her down where the waters stand.
   I picked her up and I pitched her in,
   Watched her as she floated down.

6. I started back home twixt twelve and one,
   Crying, My God, what have I done?
   I've murdered the only woman I love,
   Because she would not be my bride.

Frankie and Johnny

Frank-ie and John - ny were lov - ers,
Oh, Lord-y how they could love. They swore to be true to each
oth-er, Just as true as the stars a - bove, He was her
man, but he done her wrong.

2. Frankie and Johnny went walking,
    John in his brand new suit.
    Then, "Oh, good Lawd," says Frankie,
    "Don't my Johnny look real cute!"
        He was her man, but he done her wrong

3. Frankie, she was a good woman,
    And Johnny was a good man,
    And every dollar that she made
    Went right into Johnny's hand,
        He was her man, but he done her wrong.

4. Frankie went down to the corner,
    Just for a bucket of beer.
    She said to the fat bartender,
    "Has my lovin' man been here?"
        He was her man, but he done her wrong.

5. "I don't want to cause you no trouble,
    I don't want to tell you no lie;
    But I saw your man an hour ago,
    With a gal named Elly Bly,
        And if he's your man, he's a-doin' you wrong.

41

6. Frankie looked over the transom,
   And found, to her great surprise,
   That there on the bed sat Johnny,
   A-lovin' up Elly Bly.
       He was her man, but he done her wrong.

7. Frankie drew back her kimono;
   She took out her little forty-four;
   Root-a-toot-toot, that gal did shoot
   Right through that hardwood floor,
       She shot her man, 'cause he done her wrong.

8. "Roll me over easy,
   Roll me over slow,
   Roll me on my right side,
   'Cause the bullet hurts me so.
       I was her man, but I done her wrong."

9. Johnny he was a gambler,
   He gambled for the gain.
   The very last words he ever said were,
   "High-low Jack and the game."
       He was her man, but he done her wrong.

10. Bring out your long black coffin,
    Bring out your funeral clo'es;
    Bring back Johnny's mother;
    To the churchyard Johnny goes.
        He was her man, but he done her wrong.

11. Frankie went to his coffin,
    She looked down on his face.
    She said, "O Lawd, have mercy on me,
    I wish I could take his place,
        He was my man, and I done him wrong."

12. Oh bring on your rubber-tired hearses,
    Bring on your rubber-tired hacks,
    They're takin' Johnny to the buryin' groun'
    An' they won't bring a bit of him back;
        He was her man, but he done her wrong.

13. Frankie said to the warden,
    "What are they goin' to do?"
    The warden he said to Frankie,
    "It's the electric chair for you,
    You shot your man tho' he done you wrong."

14. The sheriff came around in the morning,
Said it was all for the best,
He said her lover Johnny was nothin'
But a doggone pest.
  He was her man, but he done her wrong.

15. The judge said to the jury,
"It's as plain as plain can be;
This woman shot her lover,
It's murder in the second degree,
  He was her man, tho' he done her wrong."

16. Now it was not murder in the second degree,
And was not murder in the third,
The woman simply dropped her man,
Like a hunter drops a bird.
  He was her man, but he done her wrong.

17. "Oh bring a thousand policemen,
Bring 'em around today,
Oh lock me in that dungeon,
And throw the keys away,
  I shot my man, 'cause he done me wrong."

18. "Yes, put me in that dungeon,
Oh put me in that cell,
Put me where the northeast wind blows
From the southeast corner of hell.
  I shot my man, 'cause he done me wrong."

19. Frankie mounted to the scaffold
As calm as a girl can be,
And turning her eyes to heaven, she said,
"Good Lord, I am coming to Thee.
  He was my man, but he done me wrong."

20. This story has no moral;
This story has no end.
This story only goes to show that
There ain't no good in men.
  They'll do you wrong, just as sure as you're born.

Poor Boy

When I went down to the riv-er, poor boy, To see the ships go by;___ My sweet-heart stood on the deck of one, Where she waved to me good - bye.___

Chorus:

> Bow down your head and cry, poor boy,
> Bow down your head and cry;
> Stop thinking about that woman you love,
> Bow down your head and cry.

2. I followed her for months and months,
   She offered me her hand;
   We were about to be married, when
   She ran off with a gamblin' man. (Chorus)

3. He came at me with a big jack-knife,
   I went for him with lead,
   And when the fight was over, poor boy,
   He lay on the ground cold and dead. (Chorus)

4. They took me to the big jail-house,
   The months and months rolled by;
   The jury found me guilty, poor boy,
   And the judge said, "You must die." (Chorus)

5. "Oh, do you bring me silver, poor boy,
   Or do you bring me gold?"
   "I bring you neither," said the man,
   "I bring you a hangman's fold." (Chorus)

6. "Oh, do you bring me pardon, poor boy,
   To turn me a-loose?"
   "I bring you nothing," said the man,
   "Except a hangman's noose." (Chorus)

7. And yet they call this justice, poor boy,
   Then justice let it be!
   I only killed a man who was
   A-fixin' to kill me. (Chorus)

The Crawdad Song

You get a line and I'll get a pole, Hon-ey,___
You get a line and I'll get a pole, Babe,___
You get a line and I'll get a pole,
We'll go down to the craw-dad hole,
Hon-ey, sug-ar ba-by mine.

(Continue, as above)

2. Yonder is a man with a pack on his back,
   Totin' all the crawdads he can pack.

3. A-settin' on the ice till my feet got hot,
   A-watchin' that crawdad rack and trot.

4. Crawdad, crawdad, you'd better go to hole,
   If I don't catch you, damn my soul.

5. Whatcha gonna do when the lake runs dry?
   Sit on the bank, and watch the crawdads die.

6. Whatcha gonna do when your man goes away?
   Get me a better one very next day.

Billie Magee Magaw

(Continue, as above)

2. Said one old crow unto his mate,
"What shall we do for grub to ate?"

3. "There lies a horse on yonder plain,
Who's by some cruel butcher slain.

4. We'll perch ourselves on his backbone,
And pick his eyes out one by one.

5. The meat we'll eat before it's stale
Till naught remains but bones and tail."

Patsy-Ory-Ory-Aye

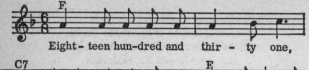

Eight - teen hun-dred and thir - ty one,

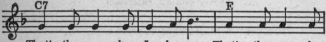

That's the year when I be-gun, That's the year when

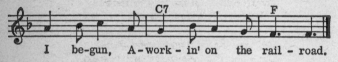

I be-gun, A-work-in' on the rail - road.

(Chorus)
Patsy Ory-ory-aye,
Patsy Ory-ory-aye,
Patsy Ory-ory-aye,
A-workin' on the railroad.

2. Eighteen hundred and thirty-two,
   Looking around for something to do,
   Looking around for something to do,
   A-workin' on the railroad.

(Continue as above)

3. Eighteen hundred and thirty-three,
   Section boss a-driving me,

4. Eighteen hundred and thirty-four,
   Hands and feet were getting sore,

5. Eighteen hundred and thirty-five,
   Felt like I was more dead than alive.

6. Eighteen hundred and thirty-six,
   Kicked a couple of dynamite sticks.
   Kicked a couple of dynamite sticks,
   And quickly left the railroad.

7. Eighteen hundred and thirty-seven,
   Found myself on the way to Heaven,
   Found myself on the way to Heaven,
   A-workin' on the railroad.

8. Eighteen hundred and thirty-eight,
   A-picking the lock in the pearly gate.

9. Eighteen hundred and thirty-nine,
   I found the angels drinking wine,
   They gave me a harp and crown divine,
   Overlooking the Railroad.

10. Eighteen hundred and thirty-ten,
    Found myself on the earth again.

11. Eighteen hundred and thirty-eleven,
    Railroad sent me again to Heaven.
    It wasn't no different than thirty-seven,
    Or workin' on the railroad.

Drill, Ye Tarriers, Drill

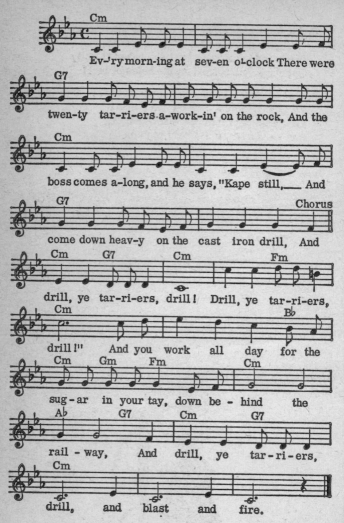

Ev-'ry morn-ing at sev-en o'clock There were
twen-ty tar-ri-ers a-work-in' on the rock, And the
boss comes a-long, and he says, "Kape still,___ And
come down heav-y on the cast iron drill, And

Chorus

drill, ye tar-ri-ers, drill! Drill, ye tar-ri-ers,
drill!" And you work all day for the
sug-ar in your tay, down be-hind the
rail-way, And drill, ye tar-ri-ers,
drill, and blast and fire.

2. The boss was a fine man down to the ground
   And he married a lady six feet 'round;
   She baked good bread, and she baked it well,
   But she baked it hard as the holes of hell!

3. Now the new foreman was Jean McCann;
   By God, he was a blamed mean man!
   Last week a premature blast went off,
   And a mile in the air went big Jim Goff.

4. The next time pay day came around,
   Jim Goff a dollar short was found.
   When he asked what for, came this reply:
   "You were docked for the time you were up in the sky."

The Ship That Never Returned

On a summer's day when the waves were rip-pling with a gen-tle and a peace-ful breeze; A— ship set sail with a car-go lad-en for a port a-cross the sea. Did she ev-er re-turn? No, she nev-er re-turned, and her fate is still un-learned, And— one last man set sail, com-man-der on a ship that nev-er re-turned.

2. There were sad farewells, there were friends forsaken,
   And her fate is still unlearned,
   But a last poor man set sail commander
   On a ship that never returned. (Chorus)

3. Said a feeble lad to his aged mother,
   "I must cross that deep blue sea,
   For I hear of a land in the far off country,
   Where there's health and strength for me." (Chorus)

4. 'Tis a gleam of hope and a maze of danger,
   And our fate is still to learn,
   And a last poor man set sail commander,
   On a ship that never returned. (Chorus)

5. Said this feeble lad to his aged mother,
   As he kissed his weeping wife,
   "Just one more purse of that golden treasure,
   It will last us all through life. (Chorus)

6. "Then we'll live in peace and joy together
   And enjoy all I have earned."
   So they sent him forth with a smile and blessing
   On a ship that never returned. (Chorus)

John Henry

When John Hen-ry was a lit-tle ba-by sit-ting on his pap-py's knee, He grabbed a ham-mer and a lit-tle piece of steel, said, "This ham-mer'll be the death of me, Oh Lord, this ham-mer'll be the death of me."

2. John Henry said to his captain
   "A man ain't nothin' but a man,
   But before I'll let your steam drill beat me down,
   I'll die with the hammer in my hand!"
   Oh Lord! Die with the hammer in my hand!

3. John Henry got his thirty-pound hammer,
   And by that steam drill he did stand,
   And he beat that steam drill three inches down,
   Then he died with his hammer in his hand!
   Oh Lord! Died with his hammer in his hand!

4. They carried John Henry to the graveyard
   And they buried him underneath the sand,
   And every locomotive goes roarin' by
   Says, "There lies a steel drivin' man!
   Oh Lord! There lies a steel drivin' man!"

Mister Froggie Went A-Courtin

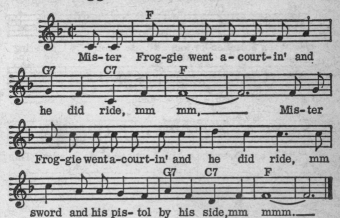

Mis-ter Frog-gie went a-court-in' and he did ride, mm mm,_____ Mis-ter Frog-gie went a-court-in' and he did ride, mm sword and his pis-tol by his side, mm mmm.____

2. So off he went with his opera hat, mm mm,
   Off he went with his opera hat, mm mm,
   So off he went with his opera hat,
   And on the way he met a rat, mm mm.

   (Continue, as above)

3. But he went on to Missy Mouse's door,
   Where he had been many times before.

4. He took Missy Mousy on his knee,
   And asked her, "Will you marry me?"

5. "Without my daddy Rat's consent,
   I wouldn't marry the President."

6. So, uncle Rat gave his consent,
   And the Weasel wrote the publishment.

7. The owl did hoot and the birds they sang,
   All through the woods the music rang.

8. What will the wedding breakfast be?
   Two green beans and a black-eyed pea.

9. They all went sailing across the brook,
   And a big white duck came and gobbled them up.

10. There's bread and cheese upon the shelf,
    If you want anymore, you can sing it yourself.

Lolly-Too-Dum

As I went out one morn-ing To take the morn-ing air, Lol-ly-too-dum, too-dum, lol-ly-too-dum day. As I went out one morn-ing To take the morn-ing air, I ov-er-heard a moth-er A-scold-in' her daugh-ter fair, Lol-ly-too-dum, too-dum, lol-ly-too-dum day.

(Continue, as above)

2. "You better go wash them dishes,
   And hush that clattering tongue,
   I know you want to get married
   And that you are too young."

3. "Oh, pity my condition
   As you would your own,
   For seventeen long years
   I've been sleeping all alone."

4. "Yes, I'm seventeen and over,
   And that you will allow--
   I must and I will get married
   For I'm in the notion now."

5. "Supposin' I was willin',
   Where would you get your man?"
   "Why, Lordy mercy, Mammy,
   I'd marry handsome Sam."

6. "Supposin' he should slight you
   Like you done him before?"
   "Why, Lordy mercy, Mammy,
   I could marry forty more."

7. "There's peddlers and there's tinkers
   And boys from the plow,
   Oh Lordy mercy, Mammy,
   I'm gettin' that feeling now!"

8. "Now my daughter's married
   And well fer to do,
   Gather 'round young fellers,
   I'm on the market too."

9. "Lordy mercy, Mammy,
   And who would marry you?
   Ain't no man alive wants
   A wife as old as you."

10. "There's doctors and there's lawyers
    And men of high degree,
    And some of them will marry
    And one will marry me."

11. "Now we both are married
    And well fer to be.
    Ha ha ha, you pretty young girls,
    That feeling's off of me."

The Blue Tail Fly

When I was young I used to wait On
mas-ter and give him his plate, And
pass the bot-tle when he got dry And
brush a-way the blue-tail fly. Jim-my crack corn and
I don't care,— Jim-my crack corn and
I don't care,— Jim-my crack corn and
I don't care, My mas-ter's gone a - way.

2. And when he'd ride in the afternoon,
   I'd follow after with a hickory broom;
   The pony being rather shy
   When bitten by the blue-tail fly. (Chorus)

3. One day he rode around the farm,
   The flies all over they did swarm.
   One chanced to bite him on the thigh.
   The devil take the blue-tail fly. (Chorus)

4. That pony run, he jump, he pitch,
   He tumble Massa in the ditch,
   He died and the jury wondered why;
   The verdict was the blue-tail fly. (Chorus)

5. They laid him under a 'simmon tree;
   His epitaph is there to see:
   "Beneath this stone I'm forced to lie,
   A victim of the blue-tail fly." (Chorus)

Eating Goober Peas

Sit-ting by the road-side on a sum-mer day, Chat-ting with my mess-mates, pas-sing time a-way, Ly-ing in the shad-ow un-der-neath the trees, Good-ness how de-lic-ious eat-ing goo-ber peas!

Peas, peas, peas, peas, eat-ing goo-ber peas.

Good-ness, how de-lic-ious eat-ing goo-ber peas!

2. Just before the battle the Gen'ral hears a row;
He says, "The Yanks are coming, I hear the rifles now."
He turns around in wonder, and what d'you think he sees?
The Tennessee Militia eating goober peas!

3. I think my song has lasted almost long enough;
The subject's interesting, but rhymes are mighty rough.
I wish the war was over, when, free from rags and fleas,
We'd kiss our wives and sweethearts and gobble goober peas!

The Riddle Song

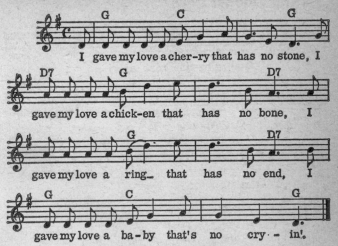

I gave my love a cher-ry that has no stone, I gave my love a chick-en that has no bone, I gave my love a ring— that has no end, I gave my love a ba-by that's no cry - in'.

2. How can there be a cherry that has no stone?
   How can there be a chicken that has no bone?
   How can there be a ring that has no end?
   How can there be a baby that's no cryin'?

3. A cherry when it's bloomin', it has no stone;
   A chicken when it's pippin', it has no bone;
   A ring when it's rollin', it has no end;
   A baby when it's sleepin', it's no cryin'.

I Wish I Was Single Again

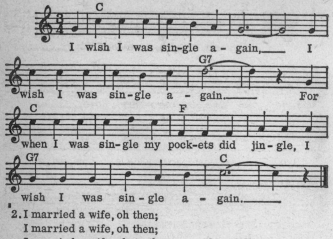

I wish I was sin-gle a - gain,___ I
wish I was sin-gle a - gain.___ For
when I was sin-gle my pock-ets did jin-gle, I
wish I was sin - gle a - gain.___

2. I married a wife, oh then;
   I married a wife, oh then;
   I married a wife, she's the curse of my life,
   I wish I was single again.

3. My wife, she died, oh then, (repeat)
   My wife, she died, and I laughed till I cried,
   To think I was single again.

   (As above)

4. I went to the funeral, and danced Yankee Doodle,
   To think I was single again.

5. I married another, the devil's grandmother,
   I wish I was single again.

6. She beat me, she banged me, she said she would hang me,
   I wish I was single again.

7. She went for the rope, when she got it, 'twas broke,
   I wish I was single again.

8. Now listen, all you young men, (repeat)
   Be good to the first, for the next will be worse,
   I wish I was single again.

Careless Love

Love, oh, love, oh, care-less love,____
Love, oh love, oh, care-less love,____
Love, oh love, oh, care - less love, See what
care - less love has done to me.____

2. When my apron strings were long,
   You passed my window with a song.

3. Now my apron strings won't tie,
   You pass my cabin door right by.

4. You pass my door, you pass my gate,
   But you won't get by my thirty-eight.

5. I cried last night and the night before
   Tonight I'll cry then cry no more.

6. What, oh what will Mother say,
   When I come home in a family way?

7. She'll tear her hair, and bite her tongue,
   For she did the same when she was young.

8. What, oh what will Daddy say?
   He ain't my real pa anyway.

9. I love my mom and daddy, too.
   But I'd leave them both to go with you.

2. The first time I seen the boll weevil,
He was settin' on the square;
The next time I seen the boll weevil,
He had all his family there.

Chorus: Just a-lookin' for a home.

3. The farmer took the boll weevil
   And buried him in hot sand;
   The boll weevil say to the farmer,
   "I'll stand it like a man."

Chorus: This'll be my home.

4. Then the farmer took the boll weevil
   And left him on the ice;
   The boll weevil say to the farmer,
   "This is mighty cool and nice."

Chorus: This'll be my home.

5. The farmer took the boll weevil
   And fed him on paris green;
   The boll weevil say to the farmer,
   "It's the best I ever seen."

Chorus: This'll be my home.

6. The boll weevil say to the farmer
   "You better let me alone;
   I et up all your cotton
   And now I'll start on the corn."

Chorus: I'll have a home.

The Foggy, Foggy Dew

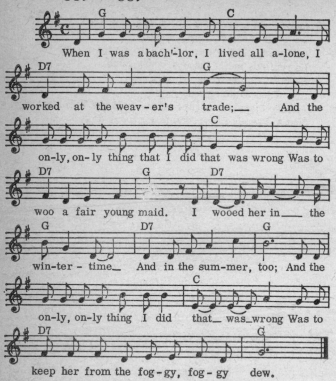

When I was a bach'-lor, I lived all a-lone, I worked at the weav-er's trade;___ And the on-ly, on-ly thing that I did that was wrong Was to woo a fair young maid. I wooed her in___ the win-ter - time___ And in the sum-mer, too; And the on-ly, on-ly thing I did that___ was___wrong Was to keep her from the fog-gy, fog-gy dew.

2. One night she knelt close by my side,
   When I was fast asleep.
   She threw her arms around my neck,
   And then began to weep.
   She wept, she cried, she tore her hair--
   Ah me, what could I do?
   So all night long I held her in my arms,
   Just to keep her from the foggy, foggy dew.

3. Again I am a bachelor, I live with my son,
   We work at the weaver's trade;
   And every single time I look into his eyes
   He reminds me of the fair young maid.
   He reminds me of the wintertime
   And of the summer too;
   And the many, many times that I held her in my arms,
   Just to keep her from the foggy, foggy dew.

Green Grow the Lilacs

Oh, green grow the li - lacs and so does the rue. How sad's been the day since I part -ed from you, But at our next meet - ing our love we'll re - new, We'll change the green li - lacs for the Red, White and Blue.

2. I once had a sweetheart but now I have none;
   He's gone off and left me to live here alone.
   He's gone off and left me contented to be;
   He must love another girl better than me.

3. On top of the mountain where green lilacs grow,
   And over the valley where the still waters flow,
   I met my true love and he proved to be true.
   We changed the green lilac for the red, white, and blue.

Red River Valley

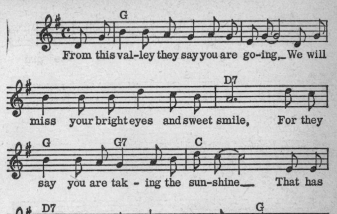

From this val-ley they say you are go-ing, We will miss your bright eyes and sweet smile, For they say you are tak-ing the sun-shine That has bright-ened our path-way a while.

2. Come and sit by my side, little darling,
Do not hasten to bid me adieu,
But remember the Red River Valley,
And the boy that has loved you so true.

3. Won't you think of the valley you're leaving?
Oh, how lonely, how sad it will be,
Oh, think of the fond heart you're breaking,
And the grief you are causing to me.

4. As you go to your home by the ocean,
May you never forget those sweet hours,
That we spent in the Red River Valley,
And the love we exchanged 'mid the flowers.

On Top of Old Smoky

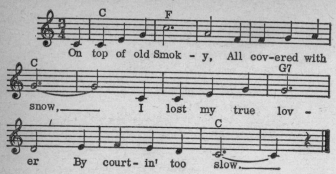

On top of old Smok - y, All cov-ered with snow,_____ I lost my true lov - er By court- in' too slow.

2. Now, courting's a pleasure,
   Parting is grief;
   But a false-hearted lover,
   Is worse than a thief.

3. A thief he will rob you
   And take all you have,
   But a false-hearted lover
   Will lead you to the grave

4. The grave will decay you
   And turn you to dust,
   There ain't one in a million
   A poor girl (boy) can trust.

5. They'll hug you and' kiss you
   And tell you more lies
   Than the cross-ties on railroads
   Or the stars in the skies.

6. They'll tell you they love you
   To give your heart ease,
   But the minute your back's turned,
   They'll court who they please.

7. I'll go back to old Smoky,
   Old Smoky so high,
   Where the wild birds and turtle doves
   Can hear my sad cry.

8. On top of old Smoky,
   All covered with snow,
   I lost my true lover
   By courtin' too slow.

9. Bury me on old Smoky,
   Old Smoky so high,
   Where the wild birds in heaven
   Can hear my sad cry.

Clementine

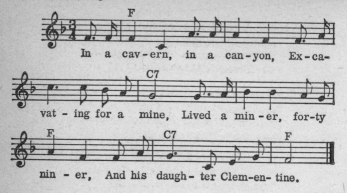

In a cav-ern, in a can-yon, Ex-ca-
vat - ing for a mine, Lived a min-er, for-ty
nin - er, And his daugh-ter Clem-en- tine.

Chorus:

Oh my darling, oh my darling,
Oh my darling Clementine,
You are lost and gone forever,
Dreadful sorry, Clementine.

2. Light she was, and like a fairy,
And her shoes were number nine,
Herring boxes without topses,
Sandals were for Clementine.

3. Drove she ducklings to the water
Every morning just at nine,
Hit her foot against a splinter,
Fell into the foaming brine.

4. Ruby lips above the water,
Blowing bubbles soft and fine,
But, alas! I was no swimmer,
So I lost my Clementine.

5. In a churchyard near the canyon,
   Where the myrtle doth entwine,
   There grow roses and other posies,
   Fertilized by Clementine.

6. Then the miner, forty-niner,
   Soon began to peak and pine;
   Though in life I used to hug her,
   Now she's dead I draw the line.

7. In my dreams she still doth haunt me,
   Robed in garments soaked with brine;
   Though in life I used to hug her,
   Now she's dead I draw the line.

8. Listen Boy Scouts, heed the warning
   To this tragic tale of mine:
   Artificial respiration
   Could have saved my Clementine.

9. How I missed her, how I missed her,
   How I missed my Clementine,
   Till I kissed her little sister,
   And forgot my Clementine.

I've Been Workin' on the Railroad

I've been work-in' on the rail - road,

All the live-long day; I've been work-in' on the

rail - road, Just to pass the time a - way.

Don't you hear the whis - tle blow - in',

Rise up so ear-ly in the morn, Don't you hear the cap-tain

shout - in': "Din - ah, blow your horn."

Din - ah, won't you blow, Din - ah, won't you blow,

Din - ah, won't you blow your horn,

Din - ah, won't you blow, Din - ah, won't you blow,

Din - ah, won't you blow your horn.

Some-one's in the kitch- en with Din - ah,

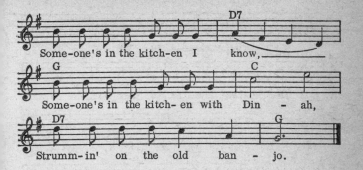

Some-one's in the kitch-en I know,

G C

Some-one's in the kitch-en with Din - ah,

D7 G

Strumm-in' on the old ban - jo.

2. Fee, fie, fiddle-i-o, fee, fie fiddle-i-o-o,
 Fee, fie, fiddle-i-o, strummin' on the old banjo.

3. Someone's makin' love to Dinah,
 Someone's makin' love I know-ow-ow-ow,
 Someone's makin' love to Dinah,
 'Cause I can't hear the old banjo.

4. Sh, sh, sh, sh, sh; sh, sh, sh, sh, sh, sh;
 Sh, sh, sh, sh, sh; I can't hear the old banjo.

My Bonnie

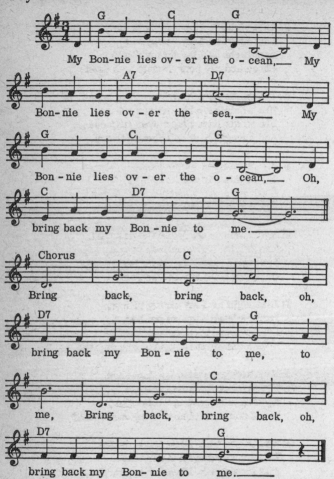

My Bon-nie lies ov-er the o-cean,___ My
Bon-nie lies ov-er the sea,___ My
Bon-nie lies ov-er the o-cean,___ Oh,
bring back my Bon-nie to me.___

Chorus
Bring back, bring back, oh,
bring back my Bon-nie to me, to
me, Bring back, bring back, oh,
bring back my Bon-nie to me.___

2. Oh, blow, ye winds, over the ocean,
And blow, ye winds, over the sea,
Oh, blow, ye winds over the ocean,
And bring back my Bonnie to me.

3. Last night as I lay on my pillow,
   Last night as I lay on my bed,
   Last night as I lay on my pillow,
   I dreamed my poor Bonnie was dead.

4. The winds have blown over the ocean,
   The winds have blown over the sea,
   The winds have blown over the ocean,
   And brought back my Bonnie to me.

5. My Bonnie has tuberculosis,
   My Bonnie has only one lung,
   My Bonnie can cough up raw oysters,
   And roll them around on her tongue.

6. My Bonnie leaned over the gas tank,
   The height of its contents to see;
   I lighted a match to assist her,
   Oh, bring back my Bonnie to me.

7. Last night as I lay on my pillow,
   Last night as I lay on my bed,
   I stuck my feet out of the window,
   Next morning the neighbors were dead.

8. My breakfast lies over the ocean,
   My luncheon lies over the rail;
   My dinner is still in commotion,
   Won't someone please bring me a pail?

9. Who knows what I had for breakfast,
   Who knows what I had for tea?
   Who knows what I had for supper,
   Just look out the window and see!
       Clams, clams, clams, clams,
       Oh, clams and ice cream don't agree with me!
       Clams, clams, clams, clams,
       Oh, clams and ice cream don't agree!

Hallelujah, I'm a Bum

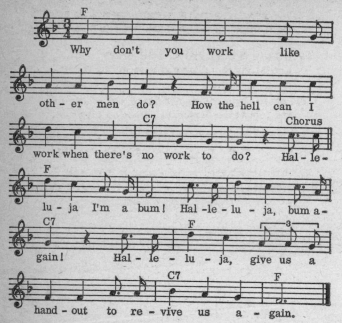

Why don't you work like oth-er men do? How the hell can I work when there's no work to do? Hal-le-lu-ja I'm a bum! Hal-le-lu-ja, bum a-gain! Hal-le-lu-ja, give us a hand-out to re-vive us a-gain.

2. Oh, I love my boss, and my boss loves me.
   And that is the reason that I'm so hungry.

3. Oh, springtime has come, and I'm just out of jail,
   Without any money, and without any bail.

4. I went to a house, and I knocked on the door,
   The lady said, "Scram, you've been here before."

5. I went to a house, and I asked for some bread;
   A lady came out, said, "The baker is dead."

6. When springtime does come, oh, won't we have fun,
   We'll throw up our jobs and we'll go on the bum.

7. If I was to work, and save all I earn,
   I could buy me a bar and have money to burn.

8. I passed by a saloon, and heard someone snore,
   And I found the bartender asleep on the floor.

9. I stayed there and drank till a copper came in,
   And he put me asleep with a slap on the chin.

10. Next morning in court I was still in a haze,
    When the judge looked at me, he said, "Thirty days."

Buffalo Gals

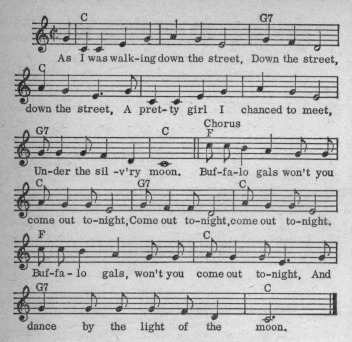

As I was walk-ing down the street, Down the street, down the street, A pret-ty girl I chanced to meet, Un-der the sil -v'ry moon.

Chorus

Buf-fa-lo gals won't you come out to-night, Come out to-night, come out to-night. Buf-fa-lo gals, won't you come out to-night, And dance by the light of the moon.

2. I asked her if she'd stop and talk,
   Stop and talk, stop and talk,
   Her feet took up the whole sidewalk,
   She was fair to view.

3. I asked her if she'd be my wife,
   Be my wife, be my wife,
   Then I'd be happy all my life,
   If she'd marry me.

Down in the Valley

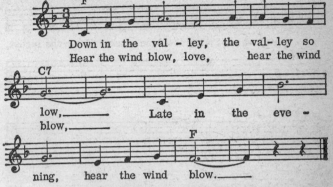

Down in the val - ley, the val- ley so
Hear the wind blow, love, hear the wind

low,_____ Late in the eve -
blow,_____

ning, hear the wind blow._____

2. If you don't love me, love whom you please,
Throw your arms 'round me, give my heart ease.
Give my heart ease, dear, give my heart ease,
Throw your arms 'round me, give my heart ease.

(As above)

3. Roses love sunshine, violets love dew;
Angels in heaven know I love you.
(Know I love you, dear, know I love you, etc.)

4. Build me a castle forty feet high,
So I can see him as he goes by.

5. Writing this letter, containing three lines,
Answer my question, "Will you be mine?"

Billy Boy

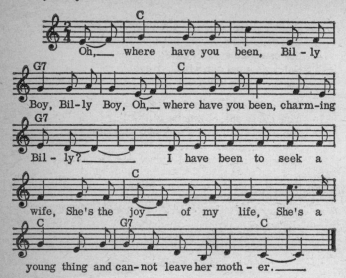

Oh,— where have you been, Bil-ly Boy, Bil-ly Boy, Oh,— where have you been, charm-ing Bil-ly?— I have been to seek a wife, She's the joy— of my life, She's a young thing and can-not leave her moth-er.—

2. Did she bid you to come in, Billy Boy, Billy Boy,
   Did she bid you to come in, charming Billy?
   Yes, she bade me to come in,
   Let me kiss her on her chin,
   She's a young thing and cannot leave her mother.

3. Did she set for you a chair, Billy Boy, Billy Boy,
   Did she set for you a chair, charming Billy?
   Yes, she set for me a chair,
   And the bottom wasn't there,
   She's a young thing and cannot leave her mother.

4. Can she bake a cherry pie, Billy Boy, Billy Boy,
Can she bake a cherry pie, charming Billy?
She can bake a cherry pie,
Quick as a cat can wink her eye,
She's a young thing and cannot leave her mother.

5. How old is she, Billy Boy, Billy Boy,
How old is she, charming Billy?
She's three times six and four times seven,
Twenty-eight and eleven,
She's a young thing and cannot leave her mother.

6. Can she sing a pretty song, Billy Boy, Billy Boy,
Can she sing a pretty song, charming Billy?
She can sing a pretty song,
But she gets the words all wrong,
She's a mother and cannot leave her young thing.

Paper of Pins

Boy: I'll give to you a paper of pins, And that's the way my love be-gins, If you will mar-ry me, me, me, If you will mar-ry me.

Girl:

2. I'll not accept your paper of pins,
   If that's the way your love begins,
   And I'll not marry you, you, you,
   For I'll not marry you.

Boy:

3. I'll give to you a dress of red
   All bound round with golden thread,
   If you will marry me, me, me,
   If you will marry me.

Girl:

4. I'll not accept your dress of red
   All bound round with golden thread,
   And I'll not marry you, you, you,
   For I'll not marry you.

Boy:

5. I'll give to you my house and land,
   My cattle and my hired man,
   If you will marry me, me. me,
   If you will marry me.

Girl:

6. I'll not accept your house and land,
   Your cattle, though the offer's grand.
   I'd love to have your hired man
   But I won't marry you.

Boy:

7. I'll give to you the key to my chest
   And all the money that I possess
   If you will marry me, me, me,
   If you will marry me.

Girl:

8. I'll take your cash, your key, and chest.
   For God's sake now please let me rest.
   Oh, yes, I'll marry you, you, you,
   But only for a week or two.

Oh, No, John

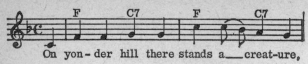

On yon-der hill there stands a___crea-ture,

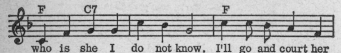

who is she I do not know. I'll go and court her

for her beau-ty, she must ans-wer yes or no.

Chorus

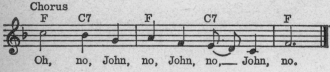

Oh, no, John, no, John, no,___ John, no.

2. My father was a Spanish captain,
   Went to sea a month ago;
   First he kissed me, then he left me;
   Told me always answer no. (Chorus)

3. Oh, madam, in your face is beauty,
   On your lips red roses' glow,
   Will you take me for your lover?
   Madam, answer yes or no. (Chorus).

4. Oh, madam, I will give you jewels,
   I will make you rich and free,
   I will give you silken dresses;
   Madam, will you marry me? (Chorus)

5. Oh, madam, since you are so cruel,
   And since you do scorn me so,
   If I may not be your lover,
   Madam, will you let me go? (Chorus)

6. Then I will stay with you forever,
   If you will not be unkind,
   Madam, I have vowed to love you,
   Would you have me change my mind? (Chorus)

7. Oh, hark, I hear the church bells ringing,
   Will you come and be my wife?
   Or, dear madam, have you settled
   To live single all your life? (Chorus)

The Frozen Logger

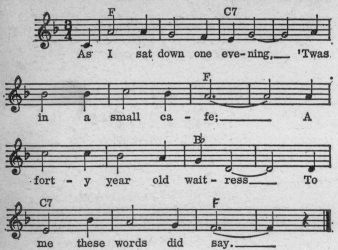

As I sat down one eve-ning,___ 'Twas in a small ca-fe;___ A fort-y year old wait-ress___ To me these words did say.___

2. I see that you're a logger,
   And not a common bum,
   For no one but a logger
   Stirs coffee with his thumb.

3. I once had a logger lover;
   There's none like him today.
   If you poured whiskey on it,
   He'd eat a bale of hay.

4. He never shaved a whisker
   Off of his horny hide;
   He hammered in the bristles,
   And bit them off inside.

Words and music by James Stevens
Copyright 1951 by Folkways Music Publishers, Inc., New York, N. Y.
USED BY PERMISSION

5. My logger came to see me,
   'Twas on a winter's day;
   He held me in a fond embrace
   That broke three vertebrae.

6. He kissed me when we parted,
   So hard it broke my jaw;
   I couldn't speak to tell him
   He forgot his mackinaw.

7. I saw my logger lover
   Go stridin' through the snow,
   A-goin' gaily homeward
   At forty-eight below.

8. The weather tried to freeze him,
   It did its very best;
   At a hundred degrees below zero,
   He buttoned up his vest.

9. It froze clear down to China,
   It froze to the stars above;
   At a thousand degrees below zero,
   It froze my logger love.

10. They tried in vain to thaw him,
    And if you believe it, sir,
    They made him into axe blades
    To cut the Douglas fir.

11. And so I lost my logger,
    And to this cafe I've come,
    And it's here I wait for someone
    To stir coffee with his thumb.

Buffalo Boy

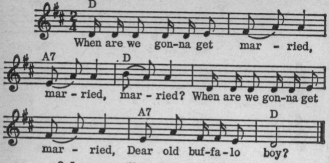

When are we gon-na get mar - ried, mar - ried, mar - ried? When are we gon-na get mar - ried, Dear old buf-fa-lo boy?

2. I guess we'll marry in a week,
   A week, a week.
   I guess we'll marry in a week,
   That is, if the weather be good.

3. How're you gonna come to the wedding,
   The wedding, the wedding?
   How're you gonna come to the wedding,
   Dear old buffalo boy?

4. I guess I'll come in my ox-cart, etc.
   That is, if the weather be good.

5. Why don't you come in your buggy, etc.
   Dear old buffalo boy?

6. My ox won't fit in the buggy, etc.
   Not even if the weather be good.

7. Who you gonna bring to the wedding, etc.
   Dear old buffalo boy?

8. I guess I'll bring my children, etc.
   That is, if the weather be good.

9. I didn't know you had no children, etc.
   Dear old buffalo boy.

10. Oh, yes, I have five children, etc.
    Six if the weather be good.

11. There ain't gonna be no wedding, etc.
    Not even if the weather be good.

Gently, Johnny, My Jingalo

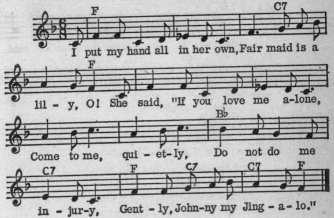

I put my hand all in her own, Fair maid is a lil - y, O! She said, "If you love me a - lone, Come to me, qui - et - ly, Do not do me in - jur-y, Gent - ly, John-ny my Jing - a - lo."

(Continue, as above)

2. I said, "You know I love you, dear."
   She whispered softly in my ear—

3. I placed my arm around her waist.
   She laughed and turned away her face.

4. I kissed her lips like rubies red,
   She blushed; then tenderly she said—

5. I slipped a ring all in her hand,
   She said, "The parson's near at hand"—

6. I took her to the church next day;
   The birds did sing, and she did say—

Two Maids Went A-Milking One Day

Two maids went a-milk - ing one day;—

Two maids went a-milk - ing one day.—

And the wind it did blow high, And the

wind it did blow low, And it toss - ed their

pails to and fro, la la la,— And it

toss - ed their pails to and fro.—

2. They met with a man they did know,
   They met with a man they did know.
   And they said, "Have you the will?"
   And they said, "Have you the skill
   For to catch us a small bird or two,
   For to catch us a small bird or two?"

3. Here's a health to the blackbird in the bush.
Likewise to the merry, merry doe.
If you will come along with me
Under yonder flowering tree,
I might catch you a small bird or two,
I might catch you a small bird or two.

4. So they went and they sat 'neath a tree.
They went and they sat 'neath two.
And the birds flew 'round about,
Pretty birds flew in and out,
And he caught them by one and by two,
And he caught them by one and by two.

5. Now my boys, let us drink down the sun,
My boys, let us drink down the moon.
Take your lady to the wood,
If you really think you should,
You might catch her a small bird or two,
You might catch her a small bird or two.

It's the Syme the Whole World Over

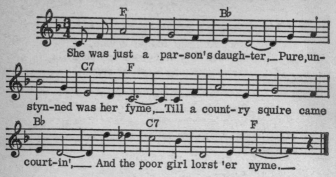

She was just a par-son's daugh-ter,—Pure, un-styn-ned was her fyme,—Till a count-ry squire came court-in',—— And the poor girl lorst 'er nyme.——

Chorus (same tune as verse):

It's the syme the whole world over,
It's the poor what gets the blyme,
While the rich 'as all the plysures,
Now ain't that a blinkin' shyme.

2. So she went aw'y to Lunnon,
Just to 'ide 'er guilty shyme.
There she met another squire,
Once ag'yn she lorst 'er nyme.

3. Look at 'im with all 'is 'orses,
Drinking champygne in 'is club,
While the wictim of 'is passions
Drinks 'er Guiness in a pub.

4. Now 'e's in 'is ridin' britches,
'Untin' foxes in the chyse,
While the wictim of 'is folly
Mykes 'er livin' by 'er wice.

5. When she tried to go from Lunnon;
   Once ag'yn to 'ide 'er shyme,
   She was 'syved' by an army chaplain,
   Once ag'yn she lorst 'er nyme.

6. 'Ear 'im as 'e jaws the Tommies,
   Warnin' o' the flymes o' 'ell.
   With 'er 'ole 'eart she 'ad trusted,
   But ag'yn she lorst 'er nyme.

7. So she settled down in Lunnon,
   Sinkin' deeper in 'er shyme,
   Till she met a lybor leader,
   And ag'yn she lorst 'er nyme.

8. Now 'e's in the 'ouse of Commons
   Mykin' laws to put down crime,
   W'ile the wictim o' 'is plysure
   Walks the street each night in shyme.

9. Then there cyme a bloated bishop
   Marriage was the tyle 'e told.
   There was no one else to tyke 'er,
   So she sold 'er soul for gold.

10. See 'er in 'er 'orse and carriage,
    Drivin' d'yly through the park.
    Though she myde a wealthy marriage,
    Still she 'ides a breakin' 'eart.

11. In a cottage down in Sussex
    Lives 'er payrents old and lyme,
    And they drink the wine she sends 'em,
    But they never speaks 'er nyme.

12. In their poor and 'umble dwelling,
    There 'er grievin' payrents live.
    Drinkin' champygne as she sends 'em
    But they never can forgive.

A cap-tain bold from Hal-i-fax, Who dwelt in coun-try quar-ters,— Se-duced a maid who hanged her-self One Mon-day in her gar-ters.— His wick-ed con-science smit-ed him, He lost his stom-ach dail-y;— He took to drink-ing rat-a-fee, And thought up-on Miss Bail-ey. Poor Miss Bail-ey, un-for-tu-nate Miss Bail-ey.

2. One night betimes he went to bed,
For he had caught a fever,
Said he, "I am a handsome man
And I'm a gay deceiver."
His candle just at twelve o'clock
Began to burn quite palely,
A ghost stepped up to his bedside
And said, "Behold! Miss Bailey!"

3. "Avaunt, Miss Bailey," then he cried,
   "You can't affright me, really."
   "Dear Captain Smith," the ghost replied,
   "You've used me ungenteelly.
   The coroner's quest was hard with me
   Because I've acted frailly,
   And Parson Biggs won't bury me,
   Though I'm a dead Miss Bailey."

4. "Miss Bailey, then, since you and I
   Accounts must once for all close,
   I've got a five-pound note
   In my regimental small-clothes.
   'Twill bribe the sexton for your grave."
   The ghost then vanished gaily,
   Crying, "Bless you, wicked Captain Smith,
   Remember poor Miss Bailey."

The Darby Ram

As I was go-ing to Dar - by Upon a mar-ket day,___ I saw the big-gest
ram, sir, That ev-er was fed on hay,___ That
ev - er was fed on hay.___

2. The ram was fat behind, sir,
   The ram was fat before,
   He measured ten yards round, sir,
   I think it was no more.

3. And he who knocked this ram down
   Was drowned in the blood,
   And he who held the dish, sir,
   Was carried away by the flood.

4. The wool grew on his back, sir,
   It reached to the sky.
   And there the eagles built their nests,
   I heard the young ones cry.

5. And all the boys in Darby, sir,
   Came begging for his eyes,
   To kick about the street, sir,
   As any good football flies.

6. The wool grew on his belly, sir,
   It reached to the ground.
   It was sold in Darby Town, sir,
   For forty thousand pound.

7. The wool upon his tail, sir,
   Filled more than fifty bags.
   You'd better keep away, sir,
   When that tail shakes and wags.

Greensleeves

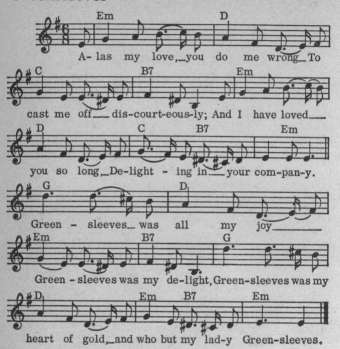

A- las my love,—you do me wrong—To
cast me off—dis-court-eous-ly; And I have loved—
you so long,—De-light - ing in—your com-pan-y.
Green - sleeves—was all my joy———
Green - sleeves was my de-light, Green-sleeves was my
heart of gold,—and who but my lad-y Green-sleeves.

2. I have been ready at your hand,
   To grant whatever you would crave;
   I have both waged life and land,
   Your love and good-will for to have.

3. If you intend thus to disdain,
   It does the more enrapture me,
   And even so, I still remain
   A lover in captivity.

4. My men were clothed all in green,
   And they did ever wait on thee;
   All this was gallant to be seen;
   And yet thou wouldst not love me.

5. Thou couldst desire no earthly thing
   But still thou hadst it readily.
   Thy music still to play and sing;
   And yet thou wouldst not love me.

6. Well, I will pray to God on high,
   That thou my constancy mayst see,
   And that yet once before I die,
   Thou wilt vouchsafe to love me.

7. Ah, Greensleeves, now farewell, adieu,
   To God I pray to prosper thee,
   For I am still thy lover true,
   Come once again and love me.

Blow the Candles Out

When I was ap-pren-ticed in Lon-don, I went to see my dear.___ The can-dles all_were burn-ing, the moon shone bright and clear. I knocked up-on her win-dow to ease her of her pain. She rose to let_me in, then she barred the door a-gain.

2. I like your well behavior and thus I often say,
   I cannot rest contented whilst you are far away.
   The roads they are so muddy, we cannot gang about,
   So roll me in your arms, love, and blow the candles out.

3. Your father and your mother in yonder room do lie,
   A-huggin' one another, so why not you and I?
   A-huggin' one another without a fear or doubt,
   So roll me in your arms, love, and blow the candles out.

4. And if you prove successful, love, pray name it after me,
   Keep it neat and kiss it sweet, and daff it on your knee.
   When my three years are ended, my time it will be out,
   Then I will double my indebtedness by blowing the candles out.

The Wee Cooper of Fife

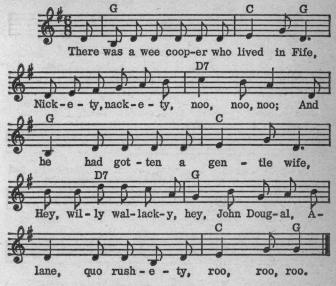

There was a wee coop-er who lived in Fife,
Nick-e-ty, nack-e-ty, noo, noo, noo; And
he had got-ten a gen-tle wife,
Hey, wil-ly wal-lack-y, hey, John Doug-al, A-
lane, quo rush-e-ty, roo, roo, roo.

(Continue, as above)

2. She would na bake nor would she brew,
   For spilin' o' her comely hue.

3. She would na caird nor would she spin,
   For shamin' o' her gentle kin.

4. The cooper has gone to his woo' pack,
   And he's laid a sheep's skin on his wife's back.

5. "I'll no be shamin' your gentle kin,
   But I will skelp my ain sheepskin."

6. "O I will bake and I will brew,
   And think nae mair o' my comely hue."

7. "O I will wash and I will spin,
   And think nae mair o' my gentle kin."

8. A' ye what hae gotten a gentle wife,
   Send ye for the wee cooper o' Fife.

The Wraggle Taggle Gypsies

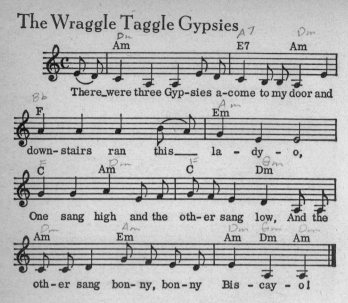

There were three Gyp-sies a-come to my door and down-stairs ran this la - dy - o, One sang high and the oth-er sang low, And the oth-er sang bon-ny, bon-ny Bis - cay - o!

2. Then she pulled off her silk-finished gown,
   And put on hose of leather-o!
   The ragged, ragged rags about our door,
   And she's gone with the wraggle-taggle Gypsies O!

3. It was late last night when my Lord came home,
   Inquiring for his a-lady, O!
   The servants said on ev'ry hand:
   She's gone with the wraggle-taggle Gypsies O!

4. O saddle to me my milk-white steed,
   And go fetch me my pony, O!
   That I may ride and seek my bride,
   Who is gone with the wraggle-taggle Gypsies O!

104

5. O he rode high, and he rode low,
   He rode through wood and copses too,
   Until he came to a wide open field,
   And there he espied his a-lady, O!

6. What makes you leave your house and land?
   What makes you leave your money O!
   What makes you leave your new wedded Lord?
   I'm off with the wraggle-taggle Gypsies O!

7. What care I for my house and land?
   What care I for my money, O!
   What care I for my new-wedded Lord?
   I'm off with the wraggle-taggle Gypsies O!

8. Last night you slept on a goose-feather bed,
   With the sheet turned down so bravely-O!
   Tonight you'll sleep in a cold, open field,
   Along with the wraggle-taggle Gypsies O!

9. What care I for a goose-feather bed,
   With the sheet turned down so bravely-O!
   For tonight I shall sleep in a cold, open field,
   Along with the wraggle-taggle Gypsies O!

The Keeper Would A-Hunting Go

The keep - er would a - hunt - ing go, And un-der his coat he car-ried a bow, All for to shoot at a mer-ry lit-tle doe, A-mong the leaves so___ green, O.

Chorus

Jack-ie boy! Mas - ter! Sing ye well? Ver-y well! Hey down! Ho down! Der-ry, der-ry down, A-mong the leaves so___ green O. To me hey down, down. To me ho down, down. Hey down! Ho down! Der-ry, der-ry down, A-mong the leaves so___ green O.

2. The first doe he shot at he missed;
The second doe he trimmed he kissed;
The third doe went where nobody wist
Among the leaves so green, O.

3. The fourth doe she did cross the plain;
The keeper fetched her back again;
Where she is now she may remain
Among the leaves so green, O.

4. The fifth doe she did cross the brook;
The keeper fetched her back with his crook;
Where she is now you must go and look
Among the leaves so green, O.

5. The sixth doe she ran over the plain;
But he with his hounds did turn her again,
And it's there he did hunt in a merry, merry vein
Among the leaves so green, O.

Cockles and Mussels

In Dub-lin's fair ci-ty where girls are so pret-ty, I first set my eyes on sweet Mol-lie Ma-lone. As she pushed her wheel bar-row Thro' streets broad and nar-row Cry-ing cock-les and mus-sels a - live, a-live oh. A - live, a - live, oh,— A - live, a-live, oh,— Cry-ing cock-les and mus-sels a - live, a - live, oh.

2. She was a fishmonger, but sure 'twas no wonder,
For so were her father and mother before,
And they each pushed their wheelbarrow
Through streets broad and narrow
Crying cockles and mussels alive, alive, oh!

3. She died of a "faver", and no one could save her,
And that was the end of sweet Mollie Malone;
Her ghost wheels her barrow
Through streets broad and narrow
Crying cockles and mussels alive, alive, oh!

The Cat and the Mouse

Oh, the liq-uor was spilled on the bar-room floor and the bar was closed for the night. When a lit-tle mouse crawled from a hole in the wall by the shad-ows of the pale moon-light. He lapped up the liq-uor on the bar-room floor and back on his haun-ches he sat. And all night long you could hear him roar: "Bring on the god-damn cat!"

2. Then a black cat came from behind the bar,
   And gobbled up the little white mouse.
   And the moral to this story is:
   Don't never take a drink on the house.

Hand Me Down My Walking Cane

Hand me down_____ my walk-in' cane,_____ Hand me down_____ my walk-in' cane,_____ Hand me down my walk-in' cane, I'm gon-na catch the mid-night train, 'Cause all my sins are tak-en a-way._____

(Continue, as above)

2. Oh, hand me down my bottle of corn,
   I'll get drunk as sure's you're born.

3. Oh, I got drunk and I landed in jail,
   And there wasn't no one to go my bail.

4. Come on, Mom, won't you go my bail,
   And get me out of this oddamn jail?

5. The meat is tough, and the beans are bad,
   Oh, my God, I can't eat that.

6. If I had listened to what you said,
   I'd be at home in my feather bed.

7. If I should die in Tennessee,
   Just send my bones home C.O.D.

8. But if I die in New York State,
   Just ship my body back by freight.

9. The devil chased me 'round a stump,
   I thought he'd catch me at every jump.

10. Oh, hell is deep, and hell is wide,
    Ain't got no bottom, ain't got no side.

Landlord, Fill the Flowing Bowl

Land-lord, fill the flow-ing bowl, un-til it doth run o-ver. Land-lord fill the flow-ing bowl, un-til it doth run o-ver. For to-night we'll mer-ry, mer-ry be, for to-night we'll mer-ry, mer-ry be, For to-night we'll mer-ry, mer-ry be, to-mor-row we'll be sob-er.

(Continue, as above)

2. The man who drinks cold water pure,
   And goes to bed quite sober,
   Falls as the leaves do fall,
   So early in October.

3. The man who drinks good whiskey clear
   And goes to bed right mellow,
   Lives as he ought to live,
   And dies a jolly good fellow.

4. But he who drinks just what he likes,
   And getteth half seas over,
   Lives until he dies, perhaps,
   And then lies down in clover.

5. The little girl who gets a kiss,
   And runs and tells her mother,
   Does a very foolish thing,
   And seldom gets another.

6. The little boy who gets a kiss
   And runs and tells his brother,
   Does a very useful thing,
   And brother gets another.

Rye Whiskey

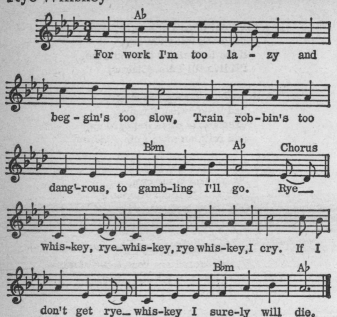

For work I'm too lazy and beg-gin's too slow, Train rob-bin's too dang'-rous, to gamb-ling I'll go. Rye— whis-key, rye—whis-key, rye whis-key, I cry. If I don't get rye— whis-key I sure-ly will die.

2. Sometimes I drink whiskey,
   Sometimes I drink wine,
   Ten thousand o' bottles
   I've killed in my time. (Chorus)

3. I've no wife to quarrel with,
   No babies to bawl,
   The best way of livin'
   Is no wife at all. (Chorus)

4. I'll eat when I'm hungry,
   I'll drink when I'm dry;
   If the hard times don't kill me,
   I'll live till I die. (Chorus)

5. Beefsteak when I'm hungry,
   Red liquor when I'm dry,
   Greenbacks when I'm hard up,
   And religion when I die. (Chorus)

6. But if I get boozy,
   My whiskey's my own,
   And them that don't like me,
   Can leave me alone. (Chorus)

7. Oh, whiskey, you villain,
   You've been my downfall,
   You've kicked me, you've cuffed me--
   But I love you for all. (Chorus)

My wife and I live all a-lone, In a
lit-tle brown hut we call our own; She loves gin and
I love rum, Oh, don't you know that we have fun?

Chorus

Ha, ha, ha, you and me, Lit-tle brown jug don't
I love thee? Ha, ha, ha, you and me,
Lit-tle brown jug don't I love thee?

2. 'Tis you who makes my friends, my foes,
   'Tis you who makes me wear old clothes,
   But here you are so near my nose,
   So tip her up and down she goes.

3. When I go toiling on my farm,
   Little brown jug under my arm,
   Place her under a shady tree,
   Little brown jug, don't I love thee?

4. I lay in the shade of a tree,
    Little brown jug in the shade of me,
    I raise her up and give a pull,
    Little brown jug's about half full.

5. Crossed the creek on a hollow log,
    Me and the wife and the little brown dog;
    The wife and the dog fell in kerplunk,
    But I held on to the little brown jug.

6. One day when I went out to my barn,
    Little brown jug under my arm,
    Tripped my toe and down I fell,
    Broke that little jug all to hell.

7. If I had a cow that gave such milk,
    I'd dress her in the finest silk,
    Feed her on the choicest hay,
    And milk her forty times a day.

8. I bought a cow from farmer Jones,
    And she was nothing but skin and bones;
    I fed her up as fine as silk,
    She jumped the fence and strained her milk.

9. When I die, don't bury me at all,
    Just pickle my bones in alcohol;
    Put a bottle o' booze at my head and feet,
    And then I know that I will keep!

10. If all the folks in Adam's race
    Were gathered together in one place
    Then I'd prepare to shed a tear
    Before I'd part with you, my dear.

11. The rose is red, my nose is too,
    The violet's blue, and so are you.
    And I guess, before I stop,
    I'd better take another drop!

Old Mountain Dew

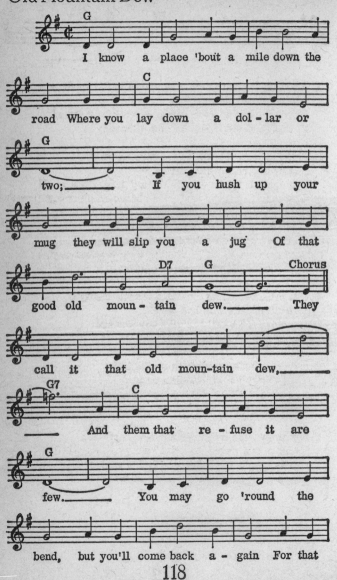

I know a place 'bout a mile down the road Where you lay down a dol-lar or two;___ If you hush up your mug they will slip you a jug Of that good old moun-tain dew.___ They call it that old moun-tain dew,___ And them that re-fuse it are few.___ You may go 'round the bend, but you'll come back a-gain For that

118

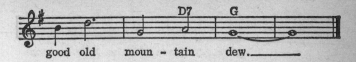

good old moun - tain dew._____

2. When its fragrance so rare starts to fill up the air
   You know that they're just about through;
   So you pucker up your lips, and you take a few sips
   Of that good old mountain dew. (Chorus)

3. Up on the hill there's an old whiskey still
   Run by a hard working crew.
   You can tell by the whiffle when you sniffle a smell,
   That they're makin' that good old mountain dew. (Chorus)

4. My brother Paul, he is tiny and small;
   He measures just about four foot two;
   But he thinks he's a gi'nt when they give him a pint
   Of that good old mountain dew. (Chorus)

5. The preacher came by with a tear in his eye,
   He said that his wife had the flu;
   We told him he ought to give her a quart
   Of that good old mountain dew. (Chorus)

6. My Uncle Bill's got a still on the hill
   Where he runs off a gallon or two;
   And the birds in the sky get so drunk they can't fly
   On that good old mountain dew. (Chorus)

7. My Aunty June tried a brand new perfume,
   It had such a sweet smelling pu.
   She was surprised when she had it analyzed,
   It was good old mountain dew. (Chorus)

There Is a Tavern in the Town

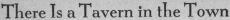

There is a tav - ern in the town, in the
town, And there my true love sits him down, sits him
down_ And_ drinks his wine as mer-ry as can
be, And nev - er, nev - er thinks of me.____

A - dieu, a-dieu, kind friends a-dieu, yes a-
dieu, I can no long-er stay with you, stay with
you; I'll_ hang my heart on a weep-ing wil-low
tree, And may the world go well with thee.____

Fare thee well, for I must leave thee, do not
let this part-ing grieve thee, And re-mem-ber that the
best of friends must part, must part.

2. He left me for a damsel dark, damsel dark,
Each Friday night they used to spark, used to spark,
And now my love who once was true to me,
Takes this dark damsel on his knee.

3. And now I see him nevermore, nevermore;
He never knocks upon my door, on my door;
Oh, woe is me; he pinned a little note,
And these were all the words he wrote:

4. Oh, dig my grave both wide and deep, wide and deep;
Put tombstones at my head and feet, head and feet,
And on my breast you may carve a turtle dove,
To signify I died for love.

Worried Man Blues

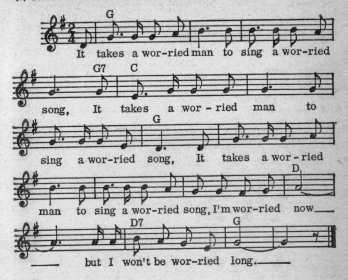

It takes a wor-ried man to sing a wor-ried song, It takes a wor-ried man to sing a wor-ried song, It takes a wor-ried man to sing a wor-ried song, I'm wor-ried now but I won't be wor-ried long.

(Continue, as above)

2. I went across the river and I lay down to sleep (three times)
   And I woke up with shackles on my feet.

3. Twenty links of chain around my leg,
   And on each link an initial of my name.

4. I asked the judge what might be my fine,
   Twenty-one years on the R.C. Mountain Line.

5. Twenty-one years to pay my awful crime,
   Twenty-one years--but I got ninety-nine.

6. The train arrived, sixteen coaches long,
   The girl I love is on that train and gone.

7. I looked down the track as far as I could see,
   Little bitty hand was waving after me.

8. If anyone should ask you who composed this song,
   Tell them it was I and I sing it all day long.

121

The St. James Infirmary

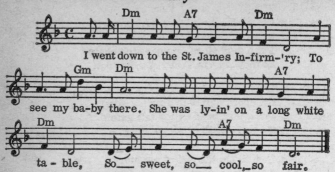

I went down to the St. James In-firm-'ry; To see my ba-by there. She was ly-in' on a long white ta-ble, So sweet, so cool, so fair.

2. Went up to see the doctor,
"She's very low," he said;
Went back to see my baby;
Great God! She was lyin' there dead.

3. I went down to old Joe's barroom,
On the corner by the square;
They were servin' the drinks as usual,
And the usual crowd was there.

4. On my left stood Joe McKennedy,
His eyes bloodshot red;
He turned to the crowd around him,
These are the words he said:

5. Let her go, let her go, God bless her;
Wherever she may be;
She may search this wide world over
She'll never find a man like me.

6. Oh, when I die, please bury me
   In my high-top Stetson hat;
   Put a gold piece on my watch chain
   So they'll know I died standin' pat.

7. Get six gamblers to carry my coffin,
   Six chorus girls to sing my song,
   Put a jazz band on my tail gate
   To raise Hell as we go along.

8. Now that's the end of my story;
   Let's have another round of booze;
   And if anyone should ask you, just tell them
   I've got the St. James Infirmary blues.

The Original Talking Blues

If you want to go to hea-ven let me tell you what to do, You got-ta grease your feet in a lit-tle mut-ton stew,__ Slide out__ of the dev-il's hand__ and ooze ov-er to the Prom-ised Land.__ Take it eas-y boy, but go grea-sy.

2. I was down in the holler just a-settin' on a log,
My finger on the trigger and my eye on a hog;
I pulled that trigger and the gun went "zip",
And I grabbed that hog with all of my grip.
'Course, I can't eat hog eyes, but I love chittlins.

2. Down in the hen house on my knees,
   I thought I heard a chicken sneeze,
   But it was only the rooster sayin' his prayers,
   Thankin' the Lord for the hens upstairs.
     Rooster prayin', hens a-layin'. Little pullets
     just pluggin' away best they know how.

3. Mama's in the kitchen fixin' the yeast,
   Poppa's in the bedroom greasin' his feet,
   Sister's in the cellar squeezin' up the hops,
   Brother's at the window just a-watchin' for the cops.
     Drinkin' home-brew makes you happy.

4. Now I'm just a city dude a-livin' out of town,
   Everybody knows me as Moonshine Brown;
   I make the beer, and I drink the slop,
   Got nine little orphans that calls me Pop.
     I'm patriotic--raisin' soldiers, Red Cross nurses.

5. Ain't no use me workin' so hard,
   I got a gal in the rich folks' yard,
   They kill a chicken, she sends me the head;
   She thinks I'm workin', I'm a-layin' up in bed.
     Just dreamin' about her. Havin' a good time...
     two other women...

Wanderin'

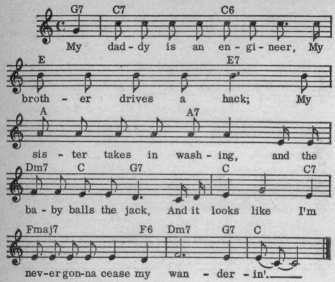

My dad-dy is an en-gi-neer, My broth-er drives a hack; My sis-ter takes in wash-ing, and the ba-by balls the jack, And it looks like I'm nev-er-gon-na cease my wan-der-in'.

2. I've been a-wanderin'
Early and late,
New York City
To the Golden Gate,
An' it looks like
I'm never gonna cease my wanderin'.

3. Been a-workin' in the army,
Workin' on a farm,
All I got to show for it
Is the muscle in my arm.
An' it looks like
I'm never gonna cease my wanderin'.

4. Snakes in the ocean,
Eels in the sea,
Red-headed woman
Made a fool out of me,
An' it looks like
I'm never gonna cease my wanderin'.

126

Every Night When the Sun Goes In

Chorus:
True love, don't weep; true love, don't mourn. (3)
I'm goin' away to Marbletown.

2. I wish to the Lord that train would come, (3)
To take me back to where I come from. (Chorus)

3. It's once my apron hung down low, (3)
He'd follow me through sleet and snow. (Chorus)

4. It's now my apron's to my chin, (3)
He'll face my door and won't come in. (Chorus)

5. I wish to the Lord my babe was born,
A-sitting upon his papa's knee,
And me, poor girl, was dead and gone,
And the green grass growing over me. (Chorus)

The Poor and the Rich

Josh-ua sat down in the temp-le of Gil-li-um,
Al-li al-li il-li-um yu-az - u-ray. He
had a bad at-tack of spi-nal men-en-gil-li-um,
Al-li al-li il-li-um yu-az - u-ray.

Chorus
Yu - az - u - ray, Yu - az - u - ray,
Al - li al - li il - li-um yu-az - u - ray.

2. A rich man lived in the city of Jerusalem,
Alli alli illium yuazuray,
He wore a silk hat and his coat was very sprucium,
Alli alli illium yuazuray. (Chorus)

(Continue, as above)

3. One day there came to his door a human wreckium,
He wore a bowler hat with the brim around his neckium.

4. The poor man begged for a piece of bread and cheesium,
The rich man said he'd call a policium.

5. The poor man died and he went up to heavium,
He danced with the angels till half-past elevium.

6. The rich man died and he went to shiolium,
Sat all day on a red hot coalium.

7. Said to the devil, "It's getting very hottium,
   Wish I had a whiskey and a sodium."

8. Devil said, "This is no hotellium,
   Just an ordinary, common old hellium."

9. The moral of the story is: Riches are no jokium,
   We'll all go to heaven 'cause we're stony brokium.

Sipping Cider Through a Straw

The pret-ti-est girl (the pret- ti - est girl), I ev - er saw (I ev - er saw), Was sip-pin' ci-(was sip-pin'ci-)der through a straw (der through a straw). The pret-ti-est girl I ev - er saw, ___ Was sip-ping ci - der through a straw.___

2. And now and then the straw would slip,
   And I'd sip cider from her lip.

3. And now I've got a mother-in-law
   From sipping cider through a straw.

4. I told that gal I didn't see how,
   She sipped that cider through a straw.

5. Then cheek to cheek, and jaw to jaw,
   We sipped that cider through a straw.

Cocaine Bill and Morphine Sue

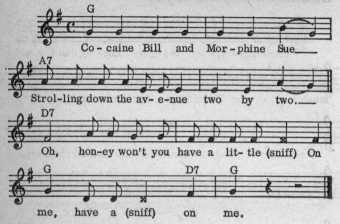

Co - caine Bill and Mor - phine Sue___

Strol-ling down the av - e-nue two by two.___

Oh, hon-ey won't you have a lit- tle (sniff) On

me, have a (sniff) on me.

2. Said Sue to Bill, "It'll do no harm,
   If we both just have a little shot in the arm."

3. Said Bill to Sue, "I can't refuse,
   'Cause there's no more kick in this darned ol' booze."

4. So they walked down First and they turned up Main,
   Looking for a place they could buy cocaine.

5. They came to a drugstore full of smoke,
   Where they saw a little sign sayin', "No more coke."

6. Now in the graveyard on the hill,
   Lies the body of Cocaine Bill.

7. And in a grave right by his side,
   Lies the body of his cocaine bride.

8. All o' you cokies is a-gonna be dead
   If you don't stop a-(sniff)ing that stuff in yo' head.

9. Now where they went, no one can tell
   It might have been Heaven or it might have been (sniff).

Grammaw's in the Cellar

Gram-maw's in the cel-lar, Lor-dy, can't you smell 'er bak-ing bis-cuits on her durned old dir-ty stove.___ In her eye there is some mat-ter that keeps drip-pin' in the bat-ter And she whis-tles while the (sniff) runs down her nose.___ Down her

Chorus

nose, (down her nose), down her nose, (down her nose), Oh, she whis-tles while the (sniff) runs down her nose. Hit the bot-tom, In her eye there is some mat-ter that keeps drip-pin' in the bat-ter And she whis-tles while the (sniff) runs down her nose.___

Away with Rum

A - way, a - way with rum, by gum, With rum, by gum, with rum, by gum. A - way, a - way, with rum, by gum, That's the song of the Sal - va - tion Arm - y. We nev - er eat cook - ies be - cause they have yeast. And one lit - tle bite turns a man in - to beast. Oh, can you i - mag - ine a sad - der dis - grace Than a man in the gut - ter with crumbs on his face.

2. We never eat fruitcake because it has rum,
   And one little slice puts a man on the bum.
   Oh, can you imagine a sorrier sight
   Than a man eating fruitcake until he is tight.

S-A-V-E-D

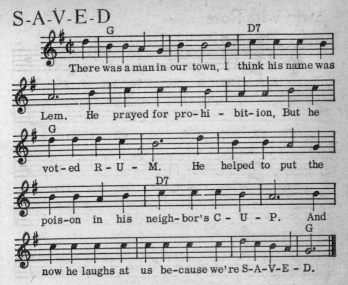

There was a man in our town, I think his name was Lem. He prayed for pro-hi-bit-ion, But he vot-ed R-U-M. He helped to put the pois-on in his neigh-bor's C-U-P. And now he laughs at us be-cause we're S-A-V-E-D.

Chorus (To approximately the same tune):

Oh, G-L-O-R-Y, we are S-A-V-E-D,
H-A-P-P-Y to be F-R-double E.
Oh, V-I-C-T-O-R-Y from the bonds of S-I-N.
Glory, Glory, Hallelujah, tra-la-la Amen.

2. Some people go on weekdays
To D-A-N-C-E.
They go to church on Sundays
To show their H-A-T.
Some people dab their faces up
With P-A-I-N-T.
And then they laugh at us
Because we're S-A-V-E-D. (Chorus)

3. I stand here on the corner
With my D-R-U-M, drum.
It brings to us the sinner
And the B-U-M, bum, bum.
They come to us from hovel
And from D-I-T-C-H.
And we march on to victory
Without H-I-T-C-H. (Chorus)

They're Moving Father's Grave

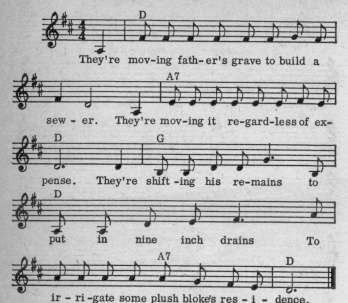

They're mov-ing fath-er's grave to build a sew - er. They're mov-ing it re-gard-less of ex-pense. They're shift-ing his re-mains to put in nine inch drains To ir - ri -gate some plush bloke's res - i - dence.

2. Now what's the use in having a religion,
   And thinking when you're dead your troubles cease,
   If some rich city chap
   Wants a pipeline to his - tank.
   And they'll never let a workman sleep in peace.

3. Now father in his life was never a quitter,
   And I don't suppose he'll be a quitter now.
   'Cause when the job's complete,
   He'll haunt that sewer sweet,
   And he'll only turn the tap when he'll allow.

4. And won't there be some bleeding consternation,
   And won't them city toffs begin to rave.
   Which is more than they deserve
   For they had the bleeding nerve
   To muck about a British workman's grave.

Hooray, They're Hanging Father

Hoo - ray, hoo - ray, my fath-er's gon-na be hung. Hoo - ray, hoo - ray, that dir - ty drunk - en bum. He was ver - y mean to me when I was ver - y young. Hoo - ray, hoo - ray, hoo - ray, hoo-ray, hoo -.ray, they're hang-ing fath - er.

2. Hooray, hooray, my mother's gonna be shot.
   Hooray, hooray, that dirty drunken sot.
   Oh, she was very mean to me when I was just a tot.
   Hooray, hooray, hooray, they're shooting mother.

3. Hooray, hooray, my uncle's gonna be hurt.
   Hooray, hooray, that nasty sex pervert.
   Oh, he was very free with me when I was just a squirt.
   Hooray, hooray, hooray, they're hurting uncle.

4. Hooray, hooray, my brother's gonna be destroyed.
   Hooray, hooray, that nasty little boy.
   He always like to try on me the things he'd read on Freud.
   Hooray, hooray, hooray, they're gonna wreck my brother.

The Dying Hobo

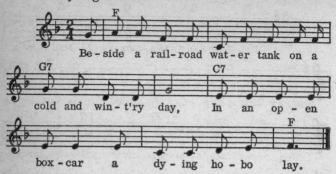

Be-side a rail-road wat-er tank on a cold and win-t'ry day, In an op-en box-car a dy-ing ho-bo lay.

2. His partner sat beside him, with low and drooping head,
   Listening to the last words the dying hobo said:

3. "I'm going," said the hobo, "to a land that's clear and bright,
   Where hammocks grow on bushes, and people stay out all night.

4. You do not have to work at all, not even change your socks,
   And little drops of alcohol came trickling down the rocks.

5. Oh, tell my gal in Denver, no more I'm gonna roam;
   I hear the fast mail coming, I'm on my way back home.

6. I hear the fast mail coming, I'll catch it bye and bye,
   Oh, gal o' mine, oh, gal o' mine, it ain't so hard to die."

7. His head fell back, his eyes fell in
   As he breathed this last refrain,
   His partner swiped his shoes and socks,
   And hopped the eastbound train.

Old King Cole

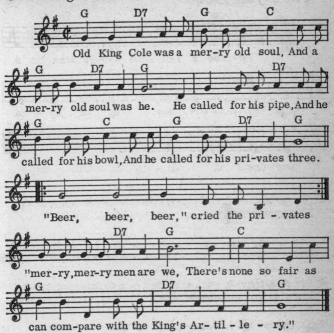

Old King Cole was a mer-ry old soul, And a mer-ry old soul was he. He called for his pipe, And he called for his bowl, And he called for his pri-vates three. "Beer, beer, beer," cried the pri-vates "mer-ry, mer-ry men are we, There's none so fair as can com-pare with the King's Ar-til-le-ry."

2. Old King Cole was a merry old soul (etc.)
   And he called for his corporals three.
   "One-two-one-two-one," said the corporals,
   "Beer, beer, beer," said the privates
   "Merry, merry men are we (etc.)

(As above, repeating previous verses
with each new verse.)

3. "Right by squads by right," said the sergeant.
4. "We do all the work," said the shavetails.
5. "We want thirty days' leave," said the captains.
6. "Bring my boots and spurs," said the majors.
7. "The Army's shot to hell," said the colonels.
8. "Shine my goddamn boots," said the generals.
9. "Praise the Lord that's all," said the chaplains.

137

A Man Without a Woman

A man_____ with-out a wo-man___ Is like a ship _____ with-out a sail,_____ Is like a boat with-out a rud-der,___ Is like a fish with-out a tail. A man_____ with-out a wo-man___ is like a wreck up-on the sand._____ But if there's one thing worse in the un-i-verse, It's a wo-man,___ I said a wo-man,___ It's a wo-man with-out a man.___

Silver Dollar©

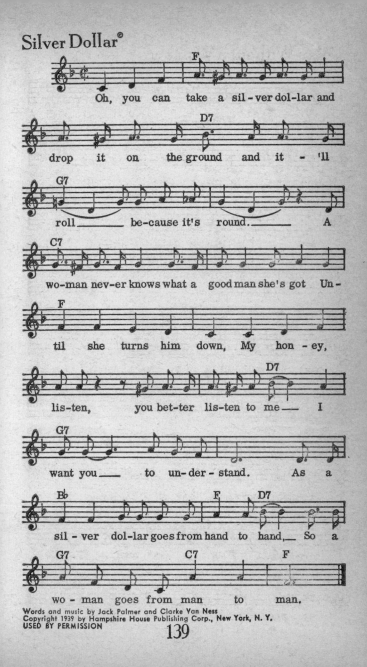

Oh, you can take a sil-ver dol-lar and
drop it on the ground and it-'ll
roll_____ be-cause it's round._____ A
wo-man nev-er knows what a good man she's got Until she turns him down, My hon-ey,
lis-ten, you bet-ter lis-ten to me___ I
want you___ to un-der-stand. As a
sil-ver dol-lar goes from hand to hand,_ So a
wo-man goes from man to man.

Words and music by Jack Palmer and Clarke Van Ness
Copyright 1939 by Hampshire House Publishing Corp., New York, N. Y.
USED BY PERMISSION

Aura Lee

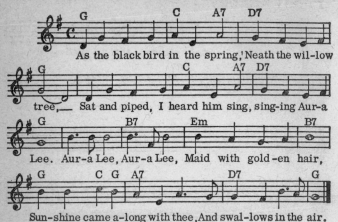

As the black bird in the spring,'Neath the wil-low tree,— Sat and piped, I heard him sing, sing-ing Aur-a Lee. Aur-a Lee, Aur-a Lee, Maid with gold-en hair, Sun-shine came a-long with thee,And swal-lows in the air.

2. In thy blush the rose was born;
Music when you spake;
Through thine azure eye the moon
Sparkling seemed to break.
Aura Lee, Aura Lee,
Birds of crimson wing
Never song have sung to me
As in that bright, sweet spring.

3. Aura Lee, the bird may flee,
The willow's golden hair
Swing through winter fitfully,
On the stormy air.
Yet if thy blue eyes I see,
Gloom will soon depart;
For to me, sweet Aura Lee
Is sunshine through the heart.

4. When the mistletoe was green,
'Midst the winter's snows,
Sunshine in thy face was seen,
Kissing lips of rose.
Aura Lee, Aura Lee,
Take my golden ring;
Love and light return with thee,
And swallows with the spring.

Paddy Murphy

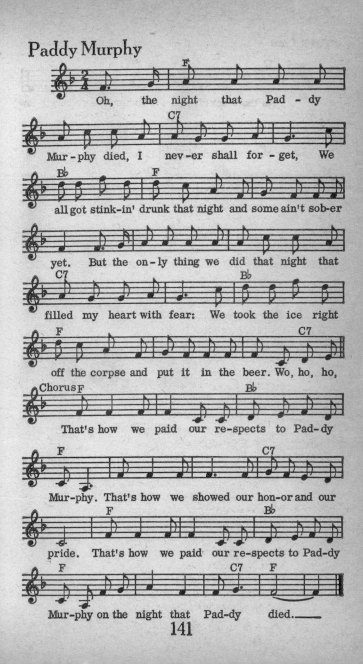

Oh, the night that Pad-dy Mur-phy died, I nev-er shall for-get, We all got stink-in' drunk that night and some ain't sob-er yet. But the on-ly thing we did that night that filled my heart with fear: We took the ice right off the corpse and put it in the beer. Wo, ho, ho,

Chorus That's how we paid our re-spects to Pad-dy Mur-phy. That's how we showed our hon-or and our pride. That's how we paid our re-spects to Pad-dy Mur-phy on the night that Pad-dy died.____

She Promised to Meet Me
When the Clock Struck Seventeen

She prom-ised to meet me when the
clock struck sev - en - teen, At the
stock-yard, just six miles out of town, Where there's
pigs eyes and pigs ears, and good old Tex-as steers Sell for
sir-loin steak at fif- ty cents a pound. She's my
hon-ey, my ba-by, she's cross-eyed she's cra-zy, She's
knock-kneed and pig-eon toed and lame, got the rheum-a-tiz ...I
know her teeth are pho - ny, from
chew - ing Swiss ba - lon - y, She's my
pick-le-faced, con-sump-tive Ma-ry Jane. Some Jane!

142

Call Out the Army and the Navy

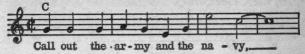

Call out the army and the na-vy,——

call out the rank and file,—— Call out the

blood-y ter-ri-tor-ials—— from the good old

Eme-rald Isle.—— Call out the

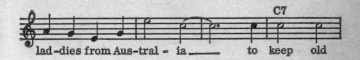

lad-dies from Aus-tral-ia—— to keep old

Eng-land free.—— Call out me

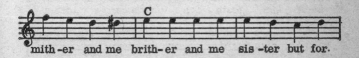

mith-er and me brith-er and me sis-ter but for.

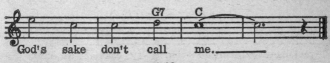

God's sake don't call me.——

143

Adam

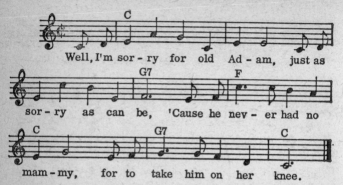

Well, I'm sor-ry for old Ad-am, just as sor-ry as can be, 'Cause he nev-er had no mam-my, for to take him on her knee.

2. And he never had no pappy, to tell him all he knowed,
Yes, he never had nobody, to point out the narrow road.

3. And he never had no childhood, playin' 'round the cabin floor,
No, he never had no mammy, for to snatch him off the floor.

4. And he never had that comfort, when at night he lay to rest
Of 'possum and sweet potatoes, tucked away beneath his vest.

5. And I've always had a feelin', he'd have let that apple be,
If he only had a mammy, for to take him on her knee.

Oh, How He Lied

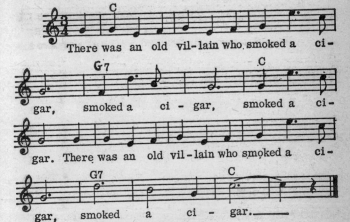

There was an old vil-lain who smoked a ci-gar, smoked a ci-gar, smoked a ci-gar. There was an old vil-lain who smoked a ci-gar, smoked a ci-gar.

2. There was a young maiden
   Who played a guitar,
   Played a guitar,
   Played a guitar,
   There was a young maiden
   Who played a guitar,
   Played a guitar.

3. He told her he loved her
   But, Oh, how he lied, (etc., as before)

4. She told him she loved him
   But she didn't lie. (etc.)

5. They were to be married
   But she up and died, (etc.)

6. He went to her funeral
   But just for the ride, (etc.)

7. He sat on her tombstone
   And boo-hoo he cried, (etc.)

8. She went up to heaven
   And flip flop, she flied, (etc.)

9. He went down to Hades
   And sizzle, he fried, (etc.)

10. Let this be a lesson
    To lovers that lie, (etc.)

The Student and the Tunnel

Rid-ing down from Ban-gor on an East-ern train,

Af - ter weeks of hunt - ing in the woods of Maine;

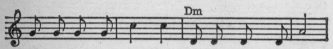

Quite ex-ten-sive whis-kers, slop-py clothes and all,

Sat a nob-le stud - ent, hand-some, dark, and tall.

2. Empty seat behind him,
   No one at his side;
   Sets him down in silence
   For a lonely ride,
   Enter aged couple,
   Take the hindmost seat;
   Enter village maiden,
   Bashful and petite.

3. Blushingly she falters,
   "Is this seat engaged?"
   Sees the aged couple
   Properly enraged.
   Student quite ecstatic
   Sees her ticket through,
   Thinking of the tunnel
   And what he will do.

4. Pleasantly they're chatting,
   While the cinders fly;
   Then the noble student
   Gets one in his eye.
   Maiden sympathetic
   Turns herself about,
   "May I, if you please, Sir,
   Try to get it out?"

5. When that noble student
   Feels her gentle touch,
   And she gently murmurs,
   "Do I hurt you much?"
   Then that noble student
   Laughs with might and main,
   As into glorious darkness
   Rides that choo-choo train.

6. Da da da da da da,
   Da da da da da, etc.

7. Out into the daylight
   Rides the choo-choo train,
   Maiden's hair is ruffled,
   Just a tiny grain,
   Student's hair is tousled,
   Tie is messed as well,
   Tiny hairpin in mustache,
   Doesn't he look swell?

Poor Lil

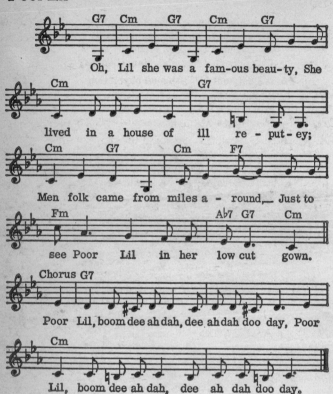

Oh, Lil she was a fam-ous beau-ty, She lived in a house of ill re-put-ey; Men folk came from miles a-round, Just to see Poor Lil in her low cut gown.

Chorus

Poor Lil, boom dee ah dah, dee ah dah doo day, Poor Lil, boom dee ah dah, dee ah dah doo day.

2. Lil was comely, Lil was fair,
   Lil had lovely golden hair,
   But she drank too deep of the demon rum
   And she smoked hasheesh and opium. (Chorus)

3. Now, day by day poor Lil grew thinner
   From insufficient proteins in 'er;
   She grew deep hollows in her chest,
   And had to go around completely dressed. (Chorus)

4. Now, clothes may make a girl go far
   But they have no place on a fille de jour.
   Oh, Lillian's troubles started when
   She concealed her abdomen. (Chorus)

5. Lillian went to the house physician;
   He prescribed for her condition:
   Madam, you have what the doctors say
   Is per-ni-shee-us a-nee-mee-ay. (Chorus)

6. So Lil took treatments in the sun;
   Lil took Scott's e-mul-si-on.
   Three times daily she took yeast,
   But still her clientele decreased. (Chorus)

7. Lillian underwent baptism;
   She adopted mysticism;
   And every night when she went to sleep
   She prayed the Lord her soul to keep. (Chorus)

8. One night as she lay in her dishonor,
   She felt the Devil's hand upon her.
   She said, "My sins I now repents,
   But, Satan, it'll cost you fifty cents." (Chorus)

Mister Reilly

Are you Mis-ter Reil-ly who keeps this ho-tel? Are
you Mis-ter Reil-ly they speaks of so well? If
you're the O'-Reil-ly they speaks of so high-ly, Gaw'
blim-ey, O'-Reil-ly you are look-ing well.

149

Ain't Gonna Grieve My Lord No More

Oh, the Deac-on went down, (Oh, the Deac-on went down) To the cel-lar to pray, (to the cel-lar to pray) He found a jug, (He found a jug) And he stayed all day, (And he stayed all day). Oh, the Deac-on went down__ to the cel-lar to pray,__ He found a jug and he stayed all day,__ I won't grieve__ my Lord ,no more,(my Lord no more). I ain't a-gon-na

grieve my Lord no more). I ain't a-gon-

grieve my Lord no more, Ain't a-gon-na

grieve_____ my Lord no more._____

2. You can't get to Heaven on roller skates,
   You'll roll right by them pearly gates.

3. You can't get to Heaven in a rocking chair,
   'Cause the Lord don't want no lazybones there.

4. You can't get to Heaven in a limousine,
   'Cause the Lord don't sell no gasoline.

5. If you get to Heaven before I do,
   Just drill a hole and pull me through.

6. If I get to Heaven before you do,
   I'll plug that hole with shavings and glue.

7. You can't get to Heaven with powder and paint,
   It makes you look like what you ain't.

8. You can't chew tobaccy on that golden shore
   The Lord don't have no cuspidor.

9. That's all there is there ain't no more,
   Saint Peter said as he closed the door.

10. There's one thing more I forgot to tell,
    If you don't go to Heaven, you'll go to Hell.

11. I'll put my grief up on the shelf,
    If you want some more make 'em up yourself.

I Was Born About Ten Thousand Years Ago

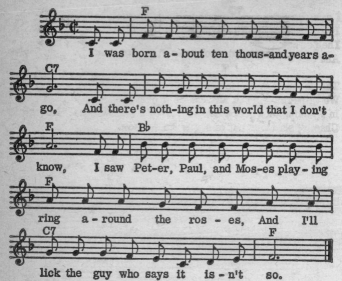

I was born a-bout ten thous-and years a-go, And there's noth-ing in this world that I don't know, I saw Pet-er, Paul, and Mos-es play-ing ring a-round the ros-es, And I'll lick the guy who says it is-n't so.

2. I saw Satan when he looked the garden o'er.
I saw Eve and Adam driven from the door,
When the apple they were eating I was 'round the corner peeking,
I can prove that I'm the guy that ate the core.

3. I saw Jonah when he shoved off in the whale,
And I thought he'd never live to tell the tale,
But old Jonah'd eaten garlic, so he gave the whale a colic
And he coughed him up and let him out of jail.

4. I saw Absalom a-hanging by the hair;
When they built the wall of China I was there.
I saved King Solomon's life and he offered me a wife.
I said, "Now you're talking business, have a chair."

5. I saw Israel in the battle of the Nile;
The arrows were flying thick and fast and wild.
I saw David with his sling pop Goliath on the wing;
I was doing forty seconds to the mile.

6. I saw Samson when he laid the village cold,
   I saw Daniel tame the lions in their hold;
   I helped build the tower of Babel up as high as they were able,
   And there's lots of other things I haven't told.

7. The queen of Sheba fell in love with me.
   We were married in Milwaukee secretly.
   In Washington I shook her, just to join with General Hooker
   Chasing skeeters out of sunny Tennessee.

The Poor Working Girl

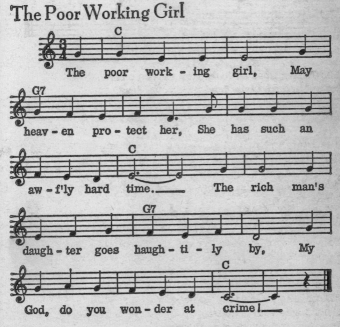

The poor work - ing girl, May
heav - en pro - tect her, She has such an
aw - f'ly hard time.___ The rich man's
daugh - ter goes haugh - ti - ly by, My
God, do you won - der at crime!___

A Cannibal Maid and Her Hottentot Blade

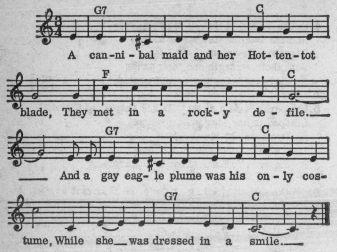

A can-ni-bal maid and her Hot-ten-tot blade, They met in a rock-y de-file.___ ___ And a gay eag-le plume was his on-ly cos-tume, While she___ was dressed in a smile.___

2. Together they strolled as his passions he told
   In thrilling and tremulous mien,
   She had murmured the word,
   When a war whoop was heard,
   And a rival burst out on the scene.

3. 'Twas a savage Zulu to the trysting place drew
   Demanding his cannibal bride,
   But the Hottentot said,
   With a toss of his head,
   "I'll have thy degenerate hide!"

4. So the Hottentot flew at the savage Zulu
   And the Zulu he flew at the blade;
   Together they vied
   With their strength and their pride
   As they fought for the cannibal maid.

5. She perched on a stone with her shapely shin bone
   Clasped in her long twining arms,
   And watched the blood fly
   With a love laden eye
   As the warriors fought for her charms.

6. Oh, the purple blood flows from the Hottentot's nose,
   And the Zulu is struck by the blade,
   As together they vied
   With their strength and their pride,
   And they died for the cannibal maid.

7. She made a fine stew of the savage Zulu
   And she scrambled the Hottentot's brains;
   'Twas a dainty menu
   When the cooking was through
   And she dined from her lover's remains.

8. Oh, the savage Zulu and the Hottentot, too,
   Are asleep in a cannibal tomb;
   The three were made one--
   My story is done,
   And the maiden walked off in the gloom.

Once There Were Three Fishermen

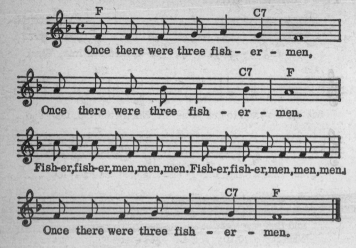

Once there were three fish - er - men,

Once there were three fish - er - men.

Fish-er, fish-er, men, men, men. Fish-er, fish-er, men, men, men.

Once there were three fish - er - men.

2. The first one's name was Abraham,
   The first one's name was Abraham,
   Abra, Abra, ham, ham, ham,
   Abra, Abra, ham, ham, ham,
   The first one's name was Abraham.

   (Continue, as above)

3. The second one's name was Isaac.
   Isey, Isey, ack, ack, ack.

4. The Third one's name was Jacob.
   Jakey, Jakey, cub, cub, cub.

5. They all sailed up to Jericho.
   Jerry, Jerry, cho, cho, cho.

6. Instead of going to Amsterdam.
   Amster, Amster, sh, sh, sh.

7. Oh, do not say that naughty word.
   Naughty, naughty, word, word, word.

156

The Persian Kitten

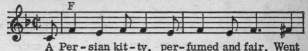

A Per-sian kit-ty, per-fumed and fair, Went

out in the yard to get some air, When a tom cat, lean and

lithe and strong, Dir-ty and rag-ged, came a-long.

2. He sniffed at the perfumed Persian cat,
   Who strutted about with much eclat,
   And thinking a bit of time to pass,
   Whispered, "Kitty, you sure got class!"

3. "That's fitting and proper," was her reply,
   As she arched her whiskers over her eye,
   "I'm rubbed, and sleep on a pillow of silk,
   Daily I'm fed on certified milk."

4. "Don't cry," said the tom cat with a smile,
   "But trust your new found friend for awhile.
   I'll show you wonders beyond your fence,
   Kitty, all you need is experience."

5. The pleasures of life he then unfurled,
   As he told her tales of the outside world,
   Suggesting at last with a leering laugh,
   A trip for the two down the primrose path.

6. The morning after the night before,
   The cat came back at the hour of four.
   The innocent look in her eye had went.
   Instead there was a look of content.

7. In after days when the children came,
   To this Persian kitty of pedigreed fame,
   They weren't Persian, they were black and tan,
   And she told 'em their daddy was a travelin' man.

John Jacob Jingleheimer Schmidt

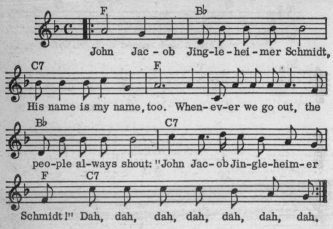

John Jac-ob Jing-le-hei-mer Schmidt,
His name is my name, too. When-ev-er we go out, the
peo-ple al-ways shout: "John Jac-ob Jin-gle-heim-er
Schmidt!" Dah, dah, dah, dah, dah, dah, dah.

My Name Is Yon Yonson

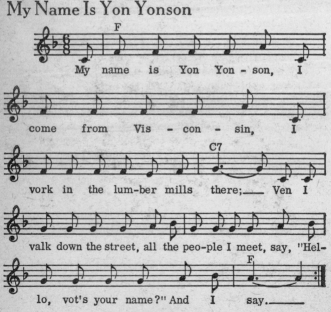

My name is Yon Yon-son, I
come from Vis-con-sin, I
vork in the lum-ber mills there;___ Ven I
valk down the street, all the peo-ple I meet, say, "Hel-
lo, vot's your name?" And I say.___

Michael Finnigin

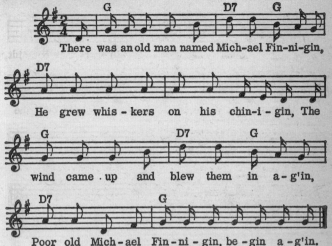

There was an old man named Mich-ael Fin-ni-gin,
He grew whis-kers on his chin-i-gin, The
wind came up and blew them in a-g'in,
Poor old Mich-ael Fin-ni-gin, be-gin a-g'in.

2. There was an old man named Michael Finnigin,
   He got drunk through drinking ginigin,
   That's how he wasted all his tinnigin,
   Poor old Michael Finnigin, begin ag'in.

3. There was an old man named Michael Finnigin,
   He grew fat and then grew thin ag'in,
   Then he died, and had to begin ag'in,
   Poor old Michael, please don't begin ag'in.

The Hokey Pokey

You put your right foot in,___ You put your right foot out,___You put your right foot in___ And shake it all a-bout, And then you do the hok-y pok-ey and you turn your-self a-bout, And that's what it's all a-bout. Hey!

(Continue, as above)   Left Hand   Right Hip
Left Foot   Right Shoulder.   Left Hip
Right Hand   Left Shoulder   Whole Self

Round the Corner

Round the cor-ner be-hind the tree___ A ser-geant maj-or he said to me: "Oh, how'd you like to mar-ry me? I would like to know, For ev-e-ry time I look in your eyes, I feel I'd like to go:

160

Alouette

A - lou-et - te, gen- tille A - lou-et - te,

A - lou- et - te, Je te plum - e - rai.

Je te plum-e-rai la tête, Je te plum-e-rai la tête;

Et la tete, Et la tête, Oh....

2. Et le bec (et le bec),
   Et la tête (et la tête, Oh...)

(Note: Continue, as above, repeating all previously
sung verses in reverse order after each new verse.)

3. Le nez

4. Le dos

5. Les jambes

6. Les pieds

7. Les pattes

8. Le cou

Was Ist Das?

Was ist das, mein Sohn, was ist das, was ist das? Das ist ein Kap-bear-er, das was es ist. Kap-bear-er Oo - la - la - loo, Das was wir learn in der schule.___

2. Was ist das, mein Sohn,
   Was ist das, was ist das?
   Das ist ein Schweat-maker,
   Das was es ist.
   Schweat-maker,
   Kap-bearer,
   Oo-la-la-loo,
   Das was wir learn in der schule.

   (Continue, as above, with the following.
   Repeat each item previously sung.)

3. Eye-seer

4. Shtink-smeller

5. Soup-strainer

6. Girl-kisser

7. Beer-holder

8. Lap-sitter

9. Rear-kicker

Schnitzelbank

Ist das nicht ein schnit-zel-bank?
Ja, das ist ein Schnit-zel-bank. Ist das nicht ein
Kurz und Lang? Ja, das ist ein Kurz und Lang.
Kurz und Lang und Schnit-zel-bank. Ei du schon-e,
ei du schon-e, Ei du schon-e Schnit-zel-bank.

2. Ist das nicht ein Hin und Her?
   Ja, das ist ein Hin und Her.
   Ist das nicht ein Lichtputzscher?
   Ja, das is ein Lichtputzscher.
   Lichtputzscher, Hin und Her, Kurz un Lang,
       und Schnitzelbank.

(Continue, as above, repeating all previously sung
verses in reverse order after each new verse.)

3. Krum und Grad, Wagenrad.
   Goldener Ring, Schones Ding.
   Gute Wurst, Grosser Durst.
   Horburgsmutter, Gute Butter.
   Besenstil, Automobile.
   Herbergavater, Gigger-Gagger.
   Helles Licht, Affengesicht.

Green Grow the Rushes

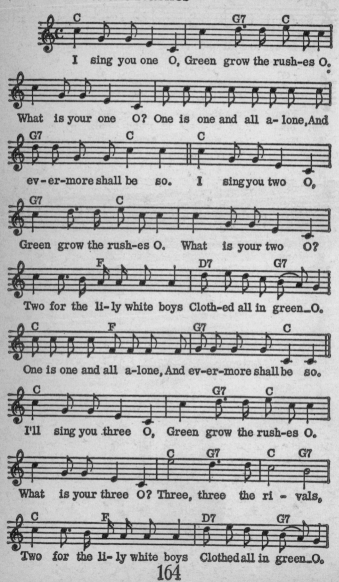

I sing you one O, Green grow the rush-es O.

What is your one O? One is one and all a-lone, And

ev-er-more shall be so. I sing you two O,

Green grow the rush-es O. What is your two O?

Two for the li-ly white boys Cloth-ed all in green O.

One is one and all a-lone, And ev-er-more shall be so.

I'll sing you three O, Green grow the rush-es O.

What is your three O? Three, three the ri-vals,

Two for the li-ly white boys Clothed all in green O.

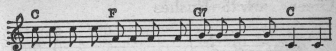

One is one and all a-lone and ev-er-more shall be so.

As above:

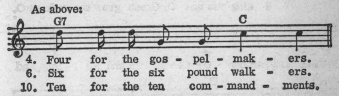

4. Four for the gos - pel - mak - ers.
6. Six for the six pound walk - ers.
10. Ten for the ten com - mand - ments.

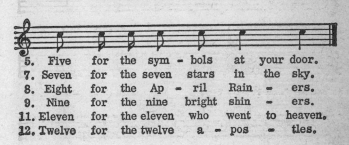

5. Five for the sym - bols at your door.
7. Seven for the seven stars in the sky.
8. Eight for the Ap - ril Rain - ers.
9. Nine for the nine bright shin - ers.
11. Eleven for the eleven who went to heaven.
12. Twelve for the twelve a - pos - tles.

165

The Twelve Days of Christmas

For each successive day repeat all the previous gifts in reverse order, always ending with "A partridge in a pear tree."

Seven swans a-swimming.

Eight maids a-milking.

Nine ladies dancing.

Ten lords a-leaping.

Eleven pipers piping.

Twelve drummers drumming.

Goodbye, My Lover, Goodbye

The ship is sail-ing down the bay, Good-
bye, my lov-er, good-bye;___ We may not meet for
man-y a day, Good-bye, my lov-er, good-
bye.___ My heart will ev-er-more be true, Good-
bye, my lov-er, good-bye;___ Tho' now we sad-ly
say a-dieu, Good-bye, my lov-er, good-bye.

Chorus
Sing-ing, Bye-low, my ba-by, bye-
low, my boun-cing ba-by boy, Sing-ing, Bye-
low, my ba-by.___ Good-bye, my lov-er, good-

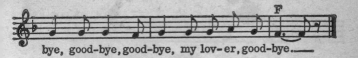

bye, good-bye, good-bye, my lov-er, good-bye.——

2. Then cheer up till we meet again,
   Good-bye my lover, good-bye;
   I'll try to bear my weary pain,
   Good-bye my lover, good-bye!

3. Tho' far I roam across the sea,
   Good-bye my lover, good-bye;
   My ev'ry thought of you shall be,
   Good-bye my lover, good-bye!

EE-LEE-AY-LEE-OH

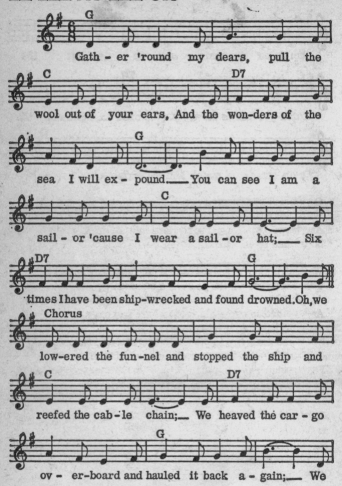

G

Gath - er 'round my dears, pull the

C   D7

wool out of your ears, And the won-ders of the

G

sea I will ex - pound.____ You can see I am a

C

sail - or 'cause I wear a sail - or hat;____ Six

D7   G

times I have been ship-wrecked and found drowned. Oh, we

Chorus

low-ered the fun-nel and stopped the ship and

C   D7

reefed the cab - le chain;__ We heaved the car - go

G

ov - er-board and hauled it back a - gain;__ We

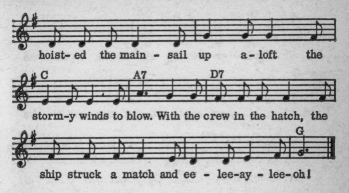

hoist-ed the main-sail up a-loft the storm-y winds to blow. With the crew in the hatch, the ship struck a match and ee-lee-ay-lee-oh!

2. On a borrowed foreign craft, silver-plated for and aft,
   With a cargo of fried eggs we did embark,
   And we were not long at sea before we struck a Christmas tree.
   So we had to eat our supper in the dark.

3. While cruising 'round the cape we had a marvelous escape;
   The wind blew off the captain's wooden leg,
   And he fell down on the deck where he nearly broke his neck
   And we had to bathe his foot in ham and eggs.

4. While the mate lay in his bunk, this ill-fated vessel sunk,
   And we all rushed up on deck to see the fun!
   For the shore we made our tracks with the cargo on our backs,
   And we sat and dried our whiskers in the sun.

The Keeper of the Eddystone Light

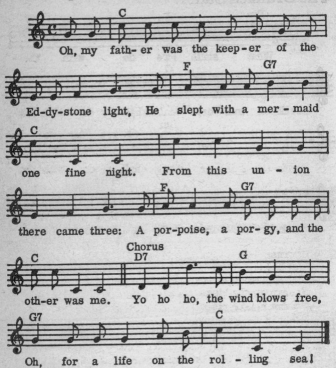

Oh, my fath-er was the keep-er of the
Ed-dy-stone light, He slept with a mer - maid
one fine night. From this un - ion
there came three: A por-poise, a por- gy, and the
oth-er was me. Yo ho ho, the wind blows free,
Oh, for a life on the rol - ling sea!

2. One night as I was a-trimmin' of the glim,
   A-singin' a verse of the evenin' hymn,
   A voice from the starboard shouted ahoy,
   And there was me mother a-sittin' on a buoy.

3. Oh, what has become of my children three,
   My mother then she asked of me.
   One was exhibited as a talking fish,
   The other was served in a chafing dish.

4. The phosphorus flashed in her seaweed hair,
   I looked again and my mother wasn't there.
   A voice came echoin' out of the night,
   "To hell with the keeper of the Eddystone Light!"

172

The Drunken Sailor

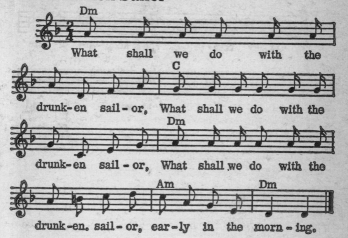

What shall we do with the drunk-en sail-or, What shall we do with the drunk-en sail-or, What shall we do with the drunk-en, sail-or, ear-ly in the morn-ing.

Chorus:

Hooray, up she rises,
Hooray, up she rises,
Hooray, up she rises,
Early in the morning.

2. Put him in the long boat till he's sober,
   Put him in the long boat, etc.

3. Pull out the plug and wet him all over.

4. Put him in the bilge and make him drink it.

5. Put him in a leaky boat and make him bale her.

6. Tie him to the scuppers with the hose pipe on him.

7. Shave his belly with a rusty razor.

8. Tie him to the topmast when she's yardarm under.

9. Heave him by the leg in a runnin' bowlin.

10. Keel haul him until he's sober.

The Er-I-E Canal

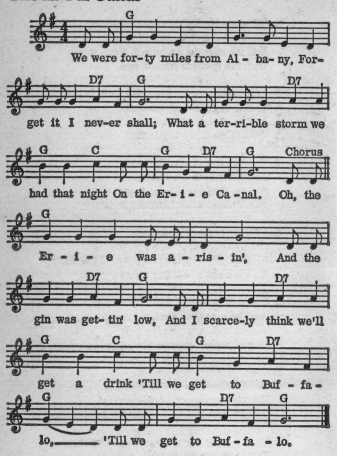

We were for-ty miles from Al – ba-ny, For-get it I nev-er shall; What a ter-ri-ble storm we had that night On the Er-i-e Ca-nal. Oh, the Er-i-e was a-ris-in', And the gin was get-tin' low, And I scarce-ly think we'll get a drink 'Till we get to Buf-fa-lo,——— 'Till we get to Buf-fa-lo.

2. We were loaded down with barley,
   We were chuck up full of rye,
   And the captain, he looked down at me
   With his goddam wicked eye.

3. Our captain, he came up on deck,
   With a spy glass in his hand,
   And the fog, it was so damn thick
   That he couldn't spy land.

4. Two days out from Syracuse
   The vessel struck a shoal
   And we like to all been foundered
   On a chunk o' Lackawanna coal.

5. We hollered to the captain
   On the towpath, tredin' dirt;
   He jumped on board and stopped the leak
   With his old red flannel shirt.

6. Our cook, she was a grand old gal,
   She had a ragged dress;
   We hoisted her upon the pole
   As a signal of distress.

7. When we got to Syracuse,
   The off-mule he was dead,
   The nigh mule got blind staggers.
   And we cracked him on the head.

8. Oh, the girls are in the Police Gazette,
   The crew are all in jail;
   And I'm the only living sea cook's son
   That's left to tell the tale.

A-Roving

In Ply-mouth Town there lived a maid, (Bless you young wo - men) In Ply-mouth Town there lived a maid, (Oh, mind what I do say) In Ply - mouth Town there lived a maid and she was mis - tress— of her trade, I'll go no more a - rov - ing with you, fair maid. A - rov - ing, a - rov - ing, Since rov-ing's been my ru - i - in, I'll go no more a— rov - ing with you, fair maid.

2. I took this fair maid for a walk,
   (Bless you young women),
   I took this fair maid for a walk,
   (Oh, mind what I do say),
   I took this fair maid for a walk
   And we had such a loving talk,
   I'll go no more a-roving with you fair maid. (Chorus)

   (Continue, as above)

3. And didn't I tell her stories, too.
   Of the gold we found in Timbuctoo. (Chorus)

4. But when we'd spent my blooming screw*,
   She cut her stick and vanished, too. (Chorus)

   (*Australian slang: paycheck)

177

The Fire Ship

As I strolled out one eve - ning out
for a night's ca - reer, I spied a lof - ty
fire - ship and af - ter her I steered; I
hoist - ed up my sig-a-nals which she ver-y quick-ly
knew, And when she see'd my bunt-ing fly, she im-
med -iate - ly hove to---o----o. She had a
dark and a rol-ling eye, And her hair hung down in
ring- a -lets, She was a nice girl, a
dec-ent girl, but one of the rov-ing kind.

2. Oh, Sir, you must excuse me for being out so late,
   For if my parents knew of it, then sad would be my fate,
   My father he's a minister, a true and honest man,
   My mother she's a Methodist, and I do the best I can.
                                                    (Chorus)

3. I took her to a tavern and I treated her to wine,
   Little did I think she belonged to the rakish kind;
   I handled her, I dandled her, and found to my surprise,
   She was nothing but a fireship rigged up in a disguise.
                                                    (Chorus)

179

(The Wreck of the) John B.

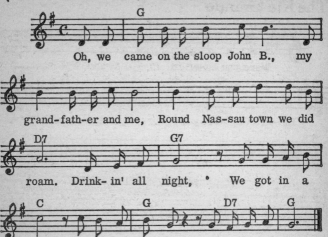

Oh, we came on the sloop John B., my grand-fath-er and me, Round Nas-sau town we did roam. Drink-in' all night, We got in a fight, I feel so break-up, I want-a go home.

(Chorus, same tune as verse):

So, hoist up the John B. sails, see how the mains'l's set,
Send for the cap'n ashore, lemme go home!
Lemme go home! Lemme go home!
I feel so break-up, I want to go home.

2. The first mate he got drunk, break up the people's trunk,
Constable come aboard and take him away,
Mr. Johnstone, please let me alone,
I feel so break-up, I want to go home.

3. The poor cook he got fits, throw 'way all the grits,
Then he took and eat up all o' my corn,
Lemme go home, I want to go home,
This is the worst trip, since I been born!

Words and music adapted by Lee Hays
From a collection by Carl Sandburg
Copyright 1950 and 1951 by Folkways Music Publishers, Inc., New York, N. Y.
USED BY PERMISSION

The Rio Grande

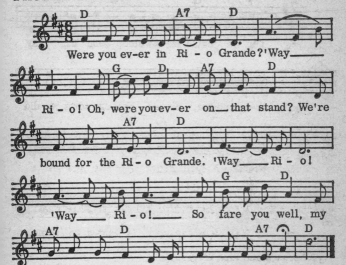

Were you ev-er in Ri - o Grande? 'Way____
Ri - o! Oh, were you ev - er on___ that stand? We're
bound for the Ri - o Grande. 'Way____ Ri - o!
'Way____ Ri - o!___ So fare you well, my
bon-ny young girl, We're bound for the Ri - o Grande.
(Continue, as above)

2. Where the Portugee girls can be found,
   And they are the girls to waltz around.

3. The anchor is weighed and the sails they are set,
   The maids we are leaving we'll never forget.

4. So pack up your sea chest and get under way,
   The girls we are leaving will get half our pay.

5. We've a jolly good ship and a jolly good crew,
   A jolly good mate and a good skipper, too.

6. Sing goodbye to Sally, and goodbye to Sue,
   And all who are listening, goodbye to you, too.

7. Man the capstan and run it around,
   We'll heave up the anchor to that jolly sound.

8. Heave with a will, heave long, and heave strong,
   And sing a good chorus for it's a good song.

Shenandoah

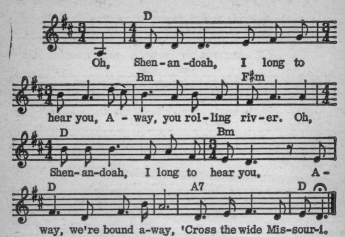

Oh, Shen-an-doah, I long to hear you, A-way, you rol-ling riv-er. Oh, Shen-an-doah, I long to hear you, A-way, we're bound a-way, 'Cross the wide Mis-sour-i.

2. The white man loved the Indian maiden,
   Away, you rolling river,
   With notions his canoe was laden,
   Away, we're bound away,
   'Cross the wide Missouri.

   (Continue, as above)

3. The chief, he made an awful holler,
   He turned away the trader's dollars.

4. Along there came a Yankee skipper,
   He winked at her and tipped his flipper.

5. He sold the chief some fire water,
   He got him drunk and stole his daughter.

6. Fare you well, I'm bound to leave you,
   Oh, Shenandoah, I'll not deceive you.

Blow the Man Down

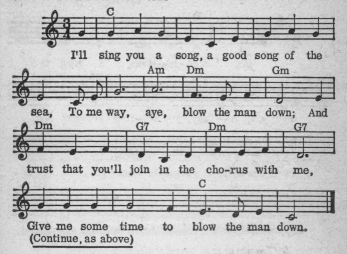

I'll sing you a song, a good song of the sea, To me way, aye, blow the man down; And trust that you'll join in the cho-rus with me, Give me some time to blow the man down.
(Continue, as above)

2. As I was a-walking down Paradise Street,
   A pretty young maiden I chanced for to meet.

3. She was round in the counter and bluff in the bow
   So I took in all sail and cried, "Way enough now!"

4. I hailed her in English, she answered me clear,
   "I'm from the Black Arrow, bound to the Shakespeare."

5. She says to me, "Will you stand treat?"
   "Delighted," says I, "for a charmer so sweet."

6. So I tailed her my flipper, and took her in tow,
   And yardarm to yardarm, away we did go.

7. I bought her a two-shilling dinner in town,
   And trinkets and laces, a bonnet and gown.

8. We walked and we talked, and her name, it was Gwen,
   I kissed her a couple, and kissed her again.

9. I says, "Will you marry a seafaring man?"
   She says, "I'll ask Mother to see if I can."

10. Along comes a sailor, they called him Half Ton,
    He says to her, "Mother," she murmurs, "My son!"

11. She says to him, "Son, here is your new daddee."
    But I says, "I'm bound for the rolling sea."

Eight Bells

My mat-ey's a sau-cy fore-top-man,— A
chum of the cook's, don't you know;— He
stuck his head down the ship's fun-nel,— And
bel-lowed, "Come up from be - low!"— Eight

Chorus

bells (eight bells), eight bells (eight bells), Rouse
up then the watch from be - low,— (be-low),— Eight
bells (eight bells), eight bells (eight bells), Rouse
up then the watch from be - low.—

2. My matey once shipped on a whaler,
   That sailed to the far northern seas;
   And being a bold-hearted sailor,
   He cared not for ice, sea, nor breeze.

3. My matey's no longer a sailor,
   But he often wakes up in the night,
   And thinking he's still on the whaler,
   Cries out in the greatest delight.

4. At the end of each watch, though, his fancy
   Was to get to his bunk quickly, O,
   For he wanted to dream of his Nancy,
   So he called to the watch, "Hi, below!"

Bell Bottomed Trousers

Once I was a lad-y's maid way down in Drur-y Lane,— My mas-ter was so kind to me, my mis-tress was the same.— A - long came a sail - or as hap - py as can be,— And he was the cause of all my mis - e - ry.—

Chorus:

Singing, "Bell-bottomed trousers, coats of navy blue,
He'll climb the riggin' like his daddy used to do."

2. He asked me for a kerchief to tie around his head,
He asked me for a candle to light his way to bed,
And I like a silly maid, thinking it no harm,
Jumped right in beside him to keep the sailor warm.

3. Early in the morning before the break of day,
A one-pound note he gave me, and this to me did say:
"Maybe you'll have a daughter, maybe you'll have a son;
Take this, oh, my darling, for the damage I have done.

4. "And if you have a daughter, bounce her on your knee;
But if you have a son, send the rascal off to sea."
The moral of the story is as plain as plain can be:
Never trust a sailor an inch above your knee.

Bury Me Not on the Lone Prairie

"Oh, bur - y me not on the lone prair - ie." These words came low and mourn - ful - ly, From the pal - lid lips of a youth who lay On his dy - ing bed at the close of day.

2. Oh bury me not on the lone prairie
   Where the kiyotes howl, and the wind blows free:
   In a narrow grave, just six by three,
   Oh bury me not on the lone prairie.

3. Oh bury me not, and his voice failed there,
   But we took no heed to his dying prayer:
   In a narrow grave just six by three
   We buried him there on the lone prairie.

4. Yes, we buried him there on the lone prairie,
   Where the old night owl hoots mournfully:
   And the blizzard howls, and the wind blows free
   O'er that lonely grave on the lone prairie.

The Streets of Laredo

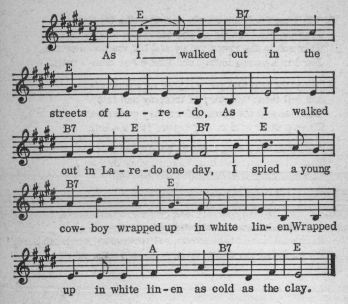

As I ____ walked out in the streets of La - re - do, As I walked out in La - re - do one day, I spied a young cow- boy wrapped up in white lin- en, Wrapped up in white lin - en as cold as the clay.

2. "I see by your outfit that you are a cowboy"--
   These words he did say as I boldly stepped by,
   "Come sit down beside me and hear my sad story;
   I was shot in the breast and I know I must die.

3. "It was once in the saddle I used to go dashing,
   It was once in the saddle I used to go gay;
   First to the dram-house and then to the card-house;
   Got shot in the breast; I am dying today.

4. "Get six jolly cowboys to carry my coffin;
   Get six pretty maidens to carry my pall;
   Put bunches of roses all over my coffin,
   Roses to deaden the clods as they fall.

5. "Oh, beat the drum slowly and play the fife lowly,
   Play the dead march as you carry me along;
   Take me to the green valley and lay the sod o'er me,
   For I'm a young cowboy and I know I've done wrong.

6. "Go gather around you a crowd of young cowboys
   And tell them the story of this, my sad fate,
   Tell one and the other before they go further
   To stop their wild roving before it's too late.

7. "Go fetch me a cup, a cup of cold water,
   To cool my parched lips," the cowboy then said;
   Before I returned, the spirit had left him
   And gone to its Maker--the cowboy was dead.

8. We beat the drum slowly and played the fife lowly,
   And bitterly wept as we bore him along;
   For we all loved our comrade, so brave, young, and handsome,
   We all loved our comrad although he'd done wrong.

The Old Chisholm Trail

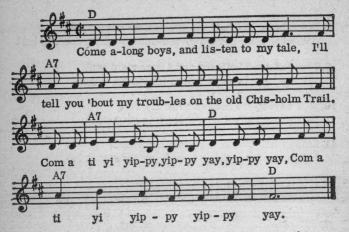

Come a-long boys, and lis-ten to my tale, I'll
tell you 'bout my troub-les on the old Chis-holm Trail.
Com a ti yi yip-py, yip-py yay, yip-py yay, Com a
ti yi yip - py yip - py yay.

2. I woke one morning on the old Chisholm Trail,
   Rope in my hand and a cow by the tail.

3. Two-dollar horse and a forty-dollar saddle,
   I could see I was ready to go punch cattle.

4. I jumped in the saddle and grabbed the horn,
   Best durn cowboy that ever was born.

5. Up in the morning before daylight,
   And before I sleep the moon shines bright.

6. Oh, it's bacon and beans most every day,
   I'd just as soon eat a pile of prairie hay.

7. It's cloudy in the west and it looks like rain,
   And my damned old slicker's in the wagon again.

8. It's raining like hell and it's getting mighty cold,
   And these long-horned so-and-sos are gettin' hard to hold.

9. I herded and I hollered and I done right well,
   Till the boss he says just to let 'em go to hell.

10. So, I went to the boss to draw my roll,
    He figured me out nine dollars in the hole.

11. I didn't like that so we had a little chat;
    I slapped him in the face with my big slouch hat.

12. So I sold my rope and I sold my saddle,
    'Cause I'm gettin' tired of punchin' these goddam cattle.

13. Goin' back to town to draw my money,
    Goin' back home to see my honey.

14. I'll ride my horse to the top of the hill,
    I'll kiss my gal, goldurn, I will.

15. My seat is in the saddle, and my saddle's in the sky;
    And I'll quit punchin' cows in the sweet by and by.

Home on the Range

Oh, give me a home where the buf-fa-lo roam, And the deer and the an-te-lope play. Where sel-dom is heard a dis-cour-a-ging word, And the skies are not cloud-y all day.

Home, home on the range, where the deer and the ant-e-lope play, Where sel-dom is heard a dis-cour-ag-ing word, And the skies are not cloud-y all day.

2. How often at night when the heavens are bright
   With the light from the glittering stars,
   Have I stood there amazed and asked as I gazed,
   If their glory exceeds that of ours.

3. Where the air is so pure, the zephyrs so free,
   The breezes so balmy and light,
   That I would not exchange my home on the range,
   For all of the cities so bright.

4. Oh, I love those wild flow'rs in this dear land of ours,
   The curlew I love to hear scream,
   And I love the white rocks and the antelope flocks,
   That graze on the mountain tops green.

Farther Along

Temp - ted and tried we're oft made to won - der, Why it should be thus all the day long. While there are oth - ers liv - ing a - bout us, Nev - er mo - lest - ed, though in the wrong.

Chorus:

Farther along we'll know all about it;
Farther along we'll understand why.
Cheer up, my brothers, live in the sunshine,
We'll understand it all by and by.

2. When death has come and taken our loved ones,
Leaving our homes so lone and so drear;
Then do we wonder why others prosper,
Living as sinners year after year. (Chorus)

3. Often I wonder why I must journey
Over a road so rugged and steep;
While there are others living in comfort,
While with the lost I labor and weep. (Chorus)

4. "Faithful till death", saith our loving Master,
   Only a while to labor and wait;
   All of our toils will soon be forgotten
   When we sweep thro' the beautiful gate. (Chorus)

5. Soon with the Lord, our wonderful Saviour
   We'll be at home beyond the blue sky;
   There we shall meet the dear ones a-waiting,
   We'll understand it all by and by. (Chorus)

Steal Away

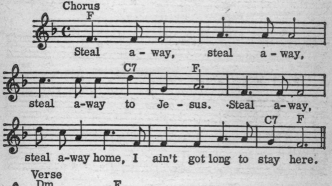

Chorus

Steal a - way, steal a - way, steal a-way to Je - sus. Steal a-way, steal a-way home, I ain't got long to stay here.

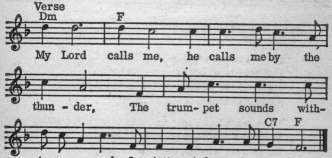

Verse

My Lord calls me, he calls me by the thun - der, The trum-pet sounds with-in-a my soul; I ain't got long to stay here.

2. Green trees are bending, poor sinner stands a-trembling.

3. My Lord calls me, He calls me by the lightning.

4. Tombstones are bursting, poor sinners stand trembling.

When the Saints Go Marching In

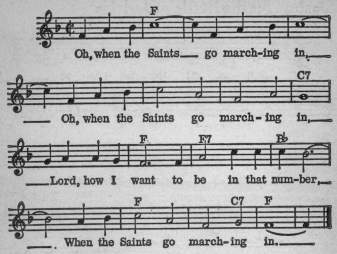

Oh, when the Saints___ go march-ing in,___

___ Oh, when the Saints go march-ing in,___

___ Lord, how I want to be in that num-ber,___

___. When the Saints go march-ing in.___

(As above)

2. And when the revelation comes.

3. Oh, when the new world is revealed.

4. Oh, when they gather 'round the throne.

5. And when they crown Him King of Kings.

6. And when the sun no more will shine.

7. And when the moon has turned to blood.

8. And on that hallelujah day.

9. And when the earth has turned to fire.

10. Oh, when the Saints go marching in.

Joshua Fit the Battle of Jericho

Josh-ua fit the bat-tle of Jer-i-cho,— Jer-i-cho,— Jer-i-cho;— Josh-ua fit the bat-tle of Jer-i-cho, And the walls came tumb-l'in' down. You may talk a-bout your kings of Gid-e-on, You may talk a-bout your men of Saul, But there's none like good old Josh-ua, At the bat-tle of Jer-i-cho.

2. Well, the Lord done told old Joshua:
   "You must do just what I say,
   March 'round that city seven times
   And the walls will tumble away."

3. So up to the walls of Jericho,
   He marched with spear in hand,
   "Go blow them ram horns," Joshua cried,
   "Cause the battle am in my hand."

4. Then the lamb, ram, sheep horns began to blow,
   And the trumpet began to sound,
   Joshua told the children to shout, that mornin'
   And the walls came tumblin' down.

Oh, Mary, Don't You Weep

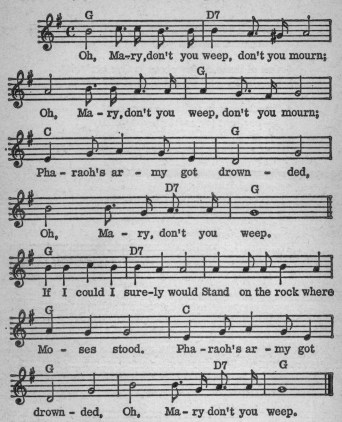

Oh, Ma-ry, don't you weep, don't you mourn;
Oh, Ma-ry, don't you weep, don't you mourn;
Pha-raoh's ar - my got drown - ded,
Oh, Ma - ry, don't you weep.
If I could I sure-ly would Stand on the rock where
Mo - ses stood. Pha-raoh's ar - my got
drown - ded, Oh, Ma-ry don't you weep.

2. Wonder what Satan's grumblin' 'bout,
   Chained in Hell an' he can't git out.
   Pharaoh's army got drownded,
   Oh, Mary, don't you weep.

   (As above)

3. Ol' Satan's mad an' I am glad,
   He missed that soul he thought he had.

198

4. Brother, better mind how you walk on the cross,
   Foot might slip and your soul get lost.

5. One of these nights about twelve o'clock,
   This old world's goin' to reel and rock.

6. I went down in the valley to pray,
   My soul got joy and I stayed all day.

7. Now don't you believe the Bible ain't true,
   'Cause you'll be sorry if you do.

8. That primrose path am wide and fair,
   Many a soul's done perished there.

Jacob's Ladder

We are climb-ing Jac-ob's lad-der,

We are climb-ing Jac-ob's lad-der,

We are climb-ing Jac-ob's lad-der,

Sol-diers of the cross.____

(As above)

2. Every round goes higher, higher.
3. Sinner, do you love my Jesus?
4. If you love him, why not serve him?
5. We are climbing higher, higher.

Go Tell It on the Mountain

Go tell it on the moun-tain, Ov-er the hills and
ev - 'ry - where,___ Go tell it on the
moun - tain That Je-sus Christ is a - gain.

Oh, when I was a sin - ner, I
prayed both night and day; I asked the Lord to
help me, and He showed me the way.

2. When I was a seeker,
   I sought both night and day;
   I asked my Lord to help me,
   And He taught me to pray.

3. He made me a watchman
   Upon the city wall;
   And if I am a Christian,
   I am the least of all.

4. It was in a lowly manger
   That Jesus Christ was born;
   The Lord sent down an angel
   That bright and glorious morn.

Swing Low, Sweet Chariot

Swing low, sweet char-i-ot,— Com-in' for to car-ry me home. Swing low, sweet char-i-ot,— Com-in' for to car-ry me home. I looked o-ver Jor-dan and what did I see,— com-in' for to car-ry me home. A band of an-gels com-in' af-ter me,— Com-in' for to car-ry me home.

2. If you get there before I do,
   Tell all my friends I'm coming, too.

3. The brightest day that ever I saw,
   When Jesus washed my sins away.

4. I'm sometimes up an' sometimes down.
   But still my soul feels heavenly boun'.

5. I never went to Heaven, but I been told
   The streets in Heaven am paved with gold.

201

All God's Chillen Got Shoes

I got a shoe, you got a shoe,

All God's chil-len got shoes; When I get to Heav-en gon-na

put on my shoes, I'm gon-na tromp all o-ver God's heav-en,

heav-en,__ heav-en,__ Ev-'ry-bod-y talk-in' 'bout

heav-en ain't a go-in' there, Heav-en,__

Heav-en,__ Gon-na tromp all ov-er God's heav-en.__

(As above)

2. I got a robe, you got a robe,
   Gonna shout all over God's heaven.

3. I got a harp, you got a harp,
   Gonna play all over God's heaven.

4. I got a song, you got a song,
   Gonna sing all over God's heaven.

5. I got wings, you got wings,
   Gonna fly all over God's heaven.

6. I got a ski, you got a ski,
   Gonna shuss all over God's heaven.

The Old Ark's A-Moverin'

Chorus

The old ark's a-mov-e-rin', a-mov-e-rin', a-mov-e-rin', The old ark's a-mov-e-rin', by the spir-it of God! The old ark's a-mov-e-rin', a-mov-e-rin', a-mov-e-rin', The old ark's a-mov-in' and I thank God.

Verse

How man-y days did the wat-er fall?—For-ty days and nights in all. Old ark she reel, Old ark she rock, Old ark she land-ed on a moun-tain top.

2. Ham, Shem, and Japheth was settin' one day,
   Talkin' on the upper deck and lookin' at the bay,
   While they was disputin' 'bout this and that,
   The Ark done bump on Ararat.

3. See that sister dressed so fine?
   She ain't got religion on her mind.
   See that brother dressed so gay?
   Devil's gonna come and carry him away.

Go Down, Moses

When Is-rael was in E-gypt's land,
Let my peo-ple go. Op-pressed. so hard they
could not stand, Let my peo-ple go.

Chorus
Go down, Mos-es, 'Way down in E-gypt's land;__
Tell__ old, Pha-raoh,__ Let my peo-ple go.

(As above)

2. Thus saith the Lord, bold Moses said,
If not I smite your firstborn dead.

3. No more shall they in bondage toil,
Let them come out with Egypt's spoil.

4. Oh, Moses, the cloud shall cleave the way,
A fire by night, a shade by day.

5. Your foes shall not before you stand,
And you'll posess fair Canaan's land.

Nobody Knows the Trouble I've Seen

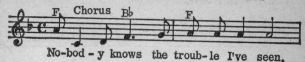

No-bod-y knows the troub-le I've seen,

no-bod-y knows but Je-sus. No-bod-y knows the

troub-le I've seen, glo-ry hal-le-lu-jah! Some-

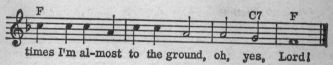

times I'm up some-times I'm down, oh, yes, Lord! Some-

times I'm al-most to the ground, oh, yes, Lord!

(As above)

2. Now, you may think that I don't know,
   But I've had my troubles here below.

3. One day when I was walkin' along,
   The sky opened up and love came down.

4. What makes old Satan hate me so?
   He had me once and had to let me go.

5. I never shall forget that day,
   When Jesus washed my sins away.

The Great Speckled Bird

What a beau - ti - ful thought I am think - ing,____ Con - cern - ing the great speck -led bird,____ 'Re - mem - ber her name is re - cord - ed____ On the pag - es of God's ho - ly Word.____

2. All the other birds flocking around her.
   And she is despised by the squad.
   But the great speckled bird in the Bible
   Is one with the great church of God.

3. All the other churches are against her.
   They envy her glory and fame,
   They hate her because she is chosen,
   And has not denied Jesus' name.

4. Desiring to lower her standard,
   They watch every move that she makes.
   They try to find fault with her teachings,
   But they can't find any mistakes.

5. She is spreading her wings for a journey,
   She's going to leave by and by.
   When the trumpet shall sound in the morning
   She'll rise and go up in the sky.

6. In the presence of all her despisers,
   With a song never uttered before,
   She will rise and be gone in a moment,
   Till the great tribulation is o'er.

7. I am glad I have learned of her meekness.
   I am glad that my name's on the book,
   And I want to be one never fearing
   On the face of my Saviour to look.

8. When He cometh descending from Heaven
   On the cloud, as is wrote in the Word,
   I'll be joyfully carried up to meet Him,
   On the wings of the great speckled bird.

Just a Closer Walk with Thee

Just a clos-er walk with Thee,_____

Grant it Jes-us if you please._____

Dail - y walk-ing close with Thee._____ Let it

be, dear Lord, let it be._____

2. Through the days of toil that's near
   If I fall dear Lord, who cares?
   Who with me my burden shares?
   None but Thee, dear Lord, None but Thee.

3. When my feeble life is o'er,
   Time for me will be no more;
   Guide me gently, safely on,
   To Thy shore, dear Lord, To Thy shore.